Nuclear Magnetic Relaxation

Frontiers in Physics

A Lecture Note and Reprint Series

DAVID PINES, *Editor*

Nuclear

Magnetic

Relaxation

A Reprint Volume

N. BLOEMBERGEN

Gordon McKay Professor of Applied Physics
Harvard University

W. A. BENJAMIN, INC.

New York   1961

NUCLEAR MAGNETIC RELAXATION
A Reprint Volume

Library of Congress Catalog Card Number: 61-18177
Manufactured in the United States of America

W. A. BENJAMIN, INC.
2465 Broadway, New York 25, New York

EDITOR'S FOREWORD

The problem of communicating in a coherent fashion the recent developments in the most exciting and active fields of physics seems particularly pressing today. The enormous growth in the number of physicists has tended to make the familiar channels of communication considerably less effective. It has become increasingly difficult for experts in a given field to keep up with the current literature; the novice can only be confused. What is needed is both a consistent account of a field and the presentation of a definite "point of view" concerning it. Formal monographs cannot meet such a need in a rapidly developing field, and, perhaps more important, the review article seems to have fallen into disfavor. Indeed, it would seem that the people most actively engaged in developing a given field are the people least likely to write at length about it.

"Frontiers in Physics" has been conceived in an effort to improve the situation in several ways. First, to take advantage of the fact that the leading physicists today frequently give a series of lectures, a graduate seminar, or a graduate course in their special fields of interest. Such lectures serve to summarize the present status of a rapidly developing field and may well constitute the only coherent account available at the time. Often, notes on lectures exist (prepared by the lecturer himself, by graduate students, or by postdoctoral fellows) and have been distributed in mimeographed form on a limited basis. One of the principal purposes of the "Frontiers in Physics" series is to make such notes available to a wider audience of physicists.

It should be emphasized that lecture notes are necessarily rough and informal, both in style and content, and those in the series will prove no exception. This is as it should be. The point of the series is to offer new, rapid, more informal, and, it is hoped, more effective ways for physicists to teach one another. The point is lost if only elegant notes qualify.

A second way to improve communication in very active fields of physics is by the publication of collections of reprints of recent articles. Such collections are themselves useful to people working in the field. The value of the reprints would, however, seem much enhanced if the collection would be accompanied by an introduction of moderate length, which would serve to tie the collection together and, necessarily, constitute a brief survey of the present status of the field. Again, it is appropriate that such an introduction be informal, in keeping with the active character of the field.

A third possibility for the series might be called an informal monograph, to connote the fact that it represents an intermediate step between lecture notes and formal monographs. It would offer the author an opportunity to present his views of a field that has developed to the point at which a summation might prove extraordinarily fruitful, but for which a formal monograph might not be feasible or desirable.

Fourth, there are the contemporary classics—papers or lectures which constitute a particularly valuable approach to the teaching and learning of physics today. Here one thinks of fields that lie at the heart of much of present-day research, but whose essentials are by now well understood, such as quantum electrodynamics or magnetic resonance. In such fields some of the best pedagogical material is not readily available, either because it consists of papers long out of print or lectures that have never been published.

"Frontiers in Physics" is designed to be flexible in editorial format. Authors are encouraged to use as many of the foregoing approaches as seem desirable for the project at hand. The publishing format for the series is in keeping with its intentions. Photo-offset printing is used throughout, and the books are paperbound, in order to speed publication and reduce costs. It is hoped that the books will thereby be within the financial reach of graduate students in this country and abroad.

Finally, because the series represents something of an experiment on the part of the editor and the publisher, suggestions from interested readers as to format, contributors, and contributions will be most welcome.

DAVID PINES

Urbana, Illinois
August 1961

PREFACE

This volume contains a photographic reproduction of my thesis (Leiden, 1948) and one research paper which appeared in *Physica*, 15, 386 (1949). No changes have been made in the original texts. All errors made by a student writing a thesis in a new field of research in a foreign language (to him) have been faithfully reproduced. A brief discussion at the end of this volume points out where major corrections are necessary. The inadequacy of my early work at the present time can best be appreciated by referring to a modern treatise on the subject, "The Principles of Nuclear Magnetism" by A. Abragam, Oxford University Press, New York, 1961. When such an excellent up-to-date account is available, the question naturally arises as to why this edition of an older work should appear at all. Historical interest alone hardly justifies such an undertaking. The answer is that there appears to be continued demand from beginning students and research workers from other branches of science, such as chemistry, biology, and medicine, for a short elementary introduction which emphasizes basic physical concepts and uses only the more rudimentary theoretical ideas. It is hoped that this volume will be helpful to those who enter the now far-flung field of magnetic relaxation, and that it may make their first steps less awkward.

Acknowledgements are reproduced with the original publications. It is a pleasure to express appreciation to the publisher, W. A. Benjamin, Inc., for their cooperation in making the present edition possible. Permission for the photographic reproduction of my thesis from the printer Schotanus & Jens N. V., Utrecht, and of the article in *Physica* from Martinus Nijhoff N. V., The Hague, is gratefully acknowledged.

N. BLOEMBERGEN

Cambridge, Massachusetts
August 1961

vii

ACKNOWLEDGMENTS

The publisher wishes to acknowledge the assistance of the following organizations in the preparation of this volume:

Martinus Nijhoff, N. V., The Hague, for permission to reproduce the article from Physica.

Schotanus & Jens N. V., Utrecht, who originally printed Dr. Bloembergen's thesis.

CONTENTS

NUCLEAR MAGNETIC
RELAXATION

The work described in this thesis was carried out at Harvard University, Cambridge, Massachusetts, in the years 1946 and 1947, under the supervision of professor P u r c e l l.

Most of the information presented here may be found in a paper to be published jointly by P u r c e l l, P o u n d and the present author in the „Physical Review". A brief account has already appeared in „Nature".

I am greatly indebted to the members of the Physics Department of Harvard University for increasing my knowledge of physics, but also for their helpfulness in other respects. Especially I would like to mention you, professor P u r c e l l. The years of cooperation and friendship with you and P o u n d I shall not forget. It is unnecessary to say how greatly I benefited in numerous discussions from the knowledge of both of you, who performed the first successful experiment of nuclear magnetic resonance, together with T o r r e y. Several discussions with professor v a n V l e c k and a stimulating course of professor S c h w i n g e r have also contributed to this thesis. The work was supported by a grant from the Research Corporation.

Mijn verblijf in Harvard zou echter minder resultaat hebben gehad, indien ik niet reeds in Utrecht de eerste schreden op het pad der experimentele natuurkunde gezet had onder Uw leiding, Hooggeleerde M i l a t z, en indien niet U, Hooggeleerde R o s e n f e l d, mij de beginselen van de theoretische physica had geleerd.

Hooggeleerde G o r t e r, dat U, wien het onderwerp van dit proefschrift zo na aan het hart ligt, mijn promotor wilt zijn, stemt mij tot grote voldoening. Dat ik U niet als eerste noem, is slechts daaraan te wijten, dat ik U niet vroeg genoeg heb leren kennen. Ik dank U voor Uw waardevolle critiek gedurende de laatste stadia van dit proefschrift.

Nog steeds ben ik dankbaar, dat het Utrechts Stedelijk Gymnasuim aan het begin van mijn studie heeft gestaan.

CONTENTS

6

ᘇᘇ

✦✦

CHAPTER I.

INTRODUCTION.

1. 1. *Nuclear spin and moments.*

The fundamental properties of a nucleus can be listed in the following way (B 1):

Mechanical properties
{
1. Mass.
2. Size.
3. Binding energy.
4. Spin.
5. Statistics.
}

Electrical properties
{
6. Charge.
7. Magnetic dipole moment.
8. Electric quadrupole moment.
}

In this thesis we shall only be concerned with properties 4, 7 and 8 of the list.

In 1924 Pauli (P 2) suggested that the hyperfine structure in atomic spectra might be explained by a small magnetic moment of the nucleus. The interaction of this magnetic dipole with the motion of the electrons would produce a hyperfine multiplet in a similar way as a multiplet is produced by interaction of the intrinsic magnetic moment of the electron with the orbital motion. The introduction of the electronic spin by Uhlenbeck and Goudsmit in 1925 made it possible to explain many hitherto mysterious details of the spectra. It appeared appropriate to connect the magnetic moment of the nuclei also with rotating charges and to attribute to the nucleus a mechanical spin. The evidence for the nuclear spin and nuclear magnetic moment is now manifold, and the concept of the spinning nucleus must be considered to be as a well founded as that of the spinning electron. The nuclear spin can be determined from the following phenomena :

1. Alternating intensities in band spectra.
2. Intensities, interval-rule and Zeeman-splitting in hyperfine multiplets.
3. Polarisation of resonance radiation.
4. Magnetic deflection in atomic and molecular beams (Stern, Rabi).

5. Total intensity of resonance absorption in nuclear paramagnetism.
6. Specific heats of (ortho- and para-) hydrogen and deuterium.
7. Scattering of identical nuclei.

The magnitude of the magnetic moment can be determined from the following experiments:

1. Splitting and Zeeman-splitting in hyperfine multiplets.
2. Magnetic deflection in molecular beams.
3. Magnetic resonance in molecular beams.
4. Nuclear paramagnetism.
5. Resonance absorbtion and dispersion in nuclear paramagnetism.
6. Ortho — para — conversion of hydrogen.

In 1935 Schüler and Schmidt (S 2) observed deviations from the interval rule in the hyperfine multiplets of Europium, which could be explained by assuming another type of interaction between the nucleus and the surrounding electrons, by means of a nuclear electric quadrupole moment. The experimental evidence for the existence of these moments has since grown, and is produced by:

1. Hyperfine spectroscopy.
2. Magnetic deflection of molecular beams (zero-moment method).
3. Fine structure of the magnetic resonance line in molecular beams.
4. Fine structure in microwave spectra.
5. Relaxation phenomena in nuclear paramagnetism,
6. Ortho — para — conversion of deuterium.

So far an influence of moments of higher order, the magnetic octupole or electric sedecipole, has not been discovered. It is, of course, outside the scope of the thesis to give even a short description of all these methods. Only the effects of nuclear paramagnetism are our topic, but we shall find opportunity to give a very brief discussion of the molecular beam method in section 1.3 and 1.5 of this introductory chapter, since these experiments are closely related to our subject. For the other fields we let follow some references, which will introduce the reader to the literature.

Kopfermann (K 5) gives a discussion of all effects which were known up to 1939 with complete references. Especially the hyperfine spectra are discussed extensively. An account of the properties of ortho — and para —, light and heavy hydrogen has been given by Farkas (F 1), the influence of the quadrupole moment of the deuteron on the ortho — para — conversion was treated by Casimir (C 1).

A field which has only recently become accessible by the development of radar techniques during the last war is microwave spectroscopy. The influence of the existence of quadrupole moments on these spectra is discussed by several authors (B 14, C 3, D 1, T 1).

⊹⊹⊹

11

The scattering of identical nuclei, especially the p—p and α—α scattering, has been discussed in numerous papers (B 3, G 1, M 4).

The nuclear spins and moments are of great interest in the theory of the constitution of the nuclei. The reader is referred to the detailed theory of the deuteron, and of H^3 and He^3 (G 2, L 3, S 1, S 4). The numerical values of the moments of these particles are explained in terms of those of the elementary particles, the neutron and proton. Some rather crude models have been built for heavier nuclei. Spin and magnetic moment also play an important role in nuclear reactions, of which we may mention the spin selection rule in β-decay, the neutron-proton scattering and the photo-magnetic desintegration of the deuteron. However in general the situation is such that the most accurate information about nuclear spins and moments is obtained from the methods mentioned in the beginning, which usually are not considered to belong to the field of nuclear physics. The results are useful to further development of nuclear theory and understanding of nuclear reactions, rather than that these latter processes yield the values of spin and moment. The case of the triton (H^3) offers an interesting illustration (A 3, B 5, S 1).

1.2. *Mathematical introduction of the nuclear spin.*

The spin is a purely quantummechanical concept. The spin angular momentum has similar properties as the orbital angular momentum. They behave in the same way under a rotation of the coordinate system and have the same commutation rules. The rules for quantisation and composition of these momenta are set forth in detail in textbooks on quantummechanics (C 4, K 6). Here we shall briefly summarize some results. The square of spin angular momentum $\vec{I}$ has the eigenvalues $I(I+1)\hbar^2$. While an orbital quantumnumber can only assume integer values, for the spin quantumnumber I also half integer values are allowed. It has been found that the spin of neutrons and protons is $1/2$, just as for the electron. The nuclear spin is generally composed of the spins of these elementary particles and their angular momenta in the nucleus. Therefore the nuclear spin I must be an integer or half integer according to whether the number of these so called nucleons is even or odd. On somewhat obscure grounds it is believed that all nuclei possessing an even number of protons and an even number of neutrons have spin zero. Experimentally this is confirmed for the lighter elements from band spectra. The experimental information for heavier isotopes only indicates that the magnetic moment, if at all present, is very small, and thus not in disagreement with a spin zero.

The nuclear spin I will, under all circumstances considered in this thesis, be a constant of the motion, since the energies involved in the processes described will never be large enough to produce transitions of the nucleus to an excited state. Only reorientations will occur. The matrices of the three components of the spin angular momentum operator transformed to the representation, in which the z-component of the operator is diagonalised, are:

$$(m \mid I_x + i\, I_y \mid m-1) = \sqrt{(I+m)\,(I-m+1)} \qquad (1.1)$$

$$(m \mid I_x - i\, I_y \mid m+1) = \sqrt{(I-m)\,(I+m+1)} \qquad (1.2)$$

$$(m \mid I_z \mid m) = m \qquad (1.3)$$

All other elements vanish.

The z-component of the spin operator has $2\,I+1$ eigenvalues $I,\ I-1,\ \ldots\ldots,-I$; m_I is called the magnetic spin quantumnumber. Not only I, but also the total electronic quantumnumber J of the atom or molecules under consideration in this book will be a constant of the motion. Processes in which the electronic state might change, will not occur. Now the angular momenta $\vec{I}$ and $\vec{J}$ combine to a resultant $\vec{F}$ in the same way, as in the case of Russell-Saunders coupling the total electronic spin $\vec{S}$ and total electronic angular momentum $\vec{L}$ combine to $\vec{J}$. The component of $\vec{F}$ on any preferred axis, which is usually taken in the z-direction, can assume the values $F,\ F-1,\ \ldots\ldots,-F$. With the angular momentum vector $\hbar\,\vec{I}$ is connected the magnetic moment vector $\vec{\mu}$. Since the two vectors behave in the same way under a rotation of the coordinate system we must have

$$\vec{\mu} = \gamma \hbar\, \vec{I} \qquad (1.4)$$

Figure 1. 1.

Coupling of the electronic and nuclear momenta in the absence of an external field.

where $\gamma = \dfrac{\text{magnetic moment}}{\text{impuls momentum}}$ is the magnetogyric ratio, which can be either positive or negative, $\gamma\,\hbar\,I$ is the maximum eigenvalue of the z-component of the magnetic moment operator and is often called the nuclear magnetic moment. $I\,\hbar$ is the maximum value of the z-component of the spin momentum vector.

13

For one free electron we have in analogy to (1. 4)

$$\vec{\mu}_{el} = \gamma_{el}\, \hbar\, \vec{S}_{el}$$

The intrinsic magnetic moment of an electron (maximum z-component) is one Bohr magneton $\beta = e\,\hbar/2\,m\,c$ and $\gamma_{el} = e/mc$ is twice the classical ratio, which holds for the orbital motion. One must not confuse γ with the dimensionless Landé-factor $g = \dfrac{\text{magnetic moment expressed in Bohr}}{\text{impuls momentum expressed in units}}$ $\dfrac{\text{magnetons}}{\hbar}$. For one free electron we have experimentally $g = 2$, which is also a result from Dirac's relativistic theory of the electron. For one or more bound electrons the total magnetic moment has in general not the same direction as the total angular momentum $\vec{J}$, as the magnetogyric ratios for spin and orbital motion are different. But the low frequency components of the magnetic moment operator, in which we shall only be interestered, can still be represented by

$$\vec{\mu} = g\,\beta\,\vec{J}$$

If the proton obeyed the Dirac equations, as the electron does, the magnetic moment of the proton would be one nuclear magneton

$$\beta_{nuc} = e\,\hbar/2\,Mc$$

Experimentally one finds that this is not true. Nevertheless the nuclear magneton gives the order of magnitude of the nuclear magnetic moments.

We list the values of spins and moments of the isotopes, used in the experiments, described in this thesis, in the following

TABLE

Nucleus	Spin	Magnetic moment	Electric quadrupole moment	Magnetogyric ratio
H^1	$I = {}^1/_2$	$\mu = 2.7896$	$Q = 0$	$\gamma = 2.673 \times 10^4$
H^2	1	0.85647	2.73×10^{-27}	0.4103×10^4
Li^7	${}^3/_2$	3.2535	?	1.039×10^4
F^{19}	${}^1/_2$	2.625	0	2.517×10^4

The impulsmomentum is expressed in units $\hbar = 1.054 \times 10^{-27}$ erg sec. The magnetic moment $\mu = \gamma\,\hbar\,I$ is expressed in units $\beta_{nuc} = 5.049 \times 10^{-24}$ erg oersted^{-1} .

The magnetogyric ratio is expressed in oersted^{-1} sec^{-1} .

The quadrupole moment Q, defined in chapter 5, is expressed in cm^2.

The spin of about 90 isotopes is known, the magnetic moment of about 50, the quadrupole moment of about 10. For the heavier isotopes usually only spectroscopic data are available. From these the values of the moments can be obtained only, when the magnetic field and the gradient of the electric field at the nucleus are known.

Now just as a Paschen-Back effect can occur in the electronic Russell-Saunders coupling, it will be possible to change the quantisation of $\vec{J}$, $\vec{I}$ and $\vec{F}$ by means of an external magnetic field. As a matter of fact it will be much easier in the latter case to decouple $\vec{J}$ and $\vec{I}$, since the interaction energy between nucleus and electron system is much smaller than between electron spin and electron orbit. In spectroscopic language one would say: the hyperfine multiplets are narrower than the multiplets. The general form of the Hamiltonian for an atom or molecule in a constant magnetic field H_o is:

$$H_{op} = A\,\gamma_I\,\hbar\,\vec{I}.\,\vec{J} + g\,\beta\,\vec{J}.\,\vec{H_0} + \gamma_I\,\hbar\,\vec{I}.\,\vec{H_0} \qquad (1.5)$$

$A\,\vec{J}$ represents the magnetic field at the position of the nucleus produced by the electronic motion. If the second or third term is large compared ot the first, a Paschen-Back effect occurs. Instead of the set of quantumnumbers I, J, F, m_F we have then the set I, J, m_I, m_J. Since the magnetic moment of the electrons is roughly 10^8 times larger than the nuclear moments, the second term is always larger than the third, unless the atom or ion is in an S-state, for which $J = 0$.

The ground state of molecules is usually a $^1\Sigma$ state. Then there is no contribution from the electron orbits and spins to the magnetic moment, but there is a small contribution from the rotation of the whole molecule. We can use the same formula (1.5). where $\vec{J}$ now stands for the rotational angular momentum of the molecule. In this case the second and third term are of the same order of magnitude.

Figure 1. 2.
Paschen-Back effect: decoupling of electronic and nuclear momenta in a strong external magnetic field.

1.3. Atomic beam deviation method.

In 1921 Stern and Gerlach let a beam

✈✈

of silver atoms pass through an inhomogeneous magnetic field. A force $\vec{K} = (\vec{\mu}.\ \text{grad})\ \vec{H}$ acted on them. The beam split in two parts. This could be explained by quantumtheory. The magnetic moment of the atoms with $J = \frac{1}{2}$ could only assume two positions with respect to the direction of the field, either parallel or antiparallel. The force acting in the cases would have opposite direction. The method is usually referred to as the atomic beam method, because usually only strong electronic moments produce a satisfactory deflection. But in 1933 Stern applied his method to hydrogen molecules (E 2, F 2). In parahydrogen the deflection is entirely caused by the rotational moment of the molecule, but in ortho-hydrogen an additional effect of the nuclear moments could be detected. It was then found that the proton moment is roughly 2. 5 times the nuclear magneton. Rabi has shown how one can obtain information about the hyperfine splitting and nuclear spin in atomic beams in spite of the presence of the large electronic moments. The values of the magnetic field must be taken so low that the coupling between $\vec{J}$ and $\vec{I}$ is not destroyed, and the first and second term in (1. 5) are of the same order. For a description of these beautiful experiments the reader is referred to Kopfermann and the original literature there mentioned.

1. 4. *The resonance principle.*

Any system possessing an angular momentum $\vec{J}$ and a magnetic moment $\vec{\mu}$, which is placed in a magnetic field rotating about the z-axis, is able to reorient itself in this field. The theory was first given by Güttinger (G 7) and Majorana (M 1) and later with more generality by Rabi and Schwinger (R 1, S 3). A more detailed discussion of this phenomenon will be given in chapter 2. Here we shall merely indicate, in a rough manner, the nature of the process involved. For this purpose we first make use of the classical picture. Let H_0 be the constant z-component of the field and H_1 the components rotating in the xy-plane.

$$H_x = H_1 \cos \omega t$$
$$H_y = H_1 \sin \omega t \qquad (1. 6)$$
$$H_z = H_0$$

We assume here $H_1 \ll H_0$. Ignoring H_1 for the moment, the magneto-mechanic system will classically precess around H_0 with the Larmor frequency

$$2 \pi \nu_0 = \omega_0 = \gamma H_0 \qquad (1. 7)$$

16

The field H_1 will exert a torque

$$\vec{T} = [\vec{\mu} \times \vec{H}_1] \qquad (1.8)$$

This torque tends to change the angle between $\vec{\mu}$ and the z-axis. If, however, H_1 and the system rotate in opposite directions, or if they do not rotate with the same frequency, the torque will soon get out of phase and after a short time interval change its sign, so that the average effect over many Larmor periods will be small. If $\omega = \omega_0$, the polar angle will gradually increase; a reorientation takes place at resonance. In the first paragraph of chapter 2 the classical description is continued in more detail.

In quantummechanical language (B 9) the effect can be described as an „optical" transition between two energy levels. We suppose that the first two terms in the Hamiltonian (1. 5) can be omitted. For molecules in a $^1\Sigma$ state in a sufficiently strong magnetic field this is certainly allowed, and it is rigorously correct for atoms or ions in a ^{1}S-state.

Figure 1.3.

Simple vector representation of a magnetic gyroscope in a large fixed magnetic field H and a small rotating field H_1, according to K e l l o g g and M i l l m a n (Rev. Mod. Phys. 18, 325, 1946).

The Hamiltonian for the problem is

$$H_{op} = - \gamma \hbar \vec{I}_{op} . \vec{H} \qquad (1.9)$$

The rotating magnetic field can be represented by

$$
\begin{aligned}
H_x + i H_y &= H_1 \, e^{+i\omega t} \\
H_x - i H_y &= H_1 \, e^{-i\omega t} \\
H_z &= H_0
\end{aligned}
\qquad (1.10)
$$

Consider the magnetic field H_1 as a small perturbation. The unperturbed Hamiltonian

$$H^0_{op} = -\gamma H_0 I_z \qquad (1.11)$$

has $2I+1$ eigenvalues, corresponding to the $2I+1$ diagonal matrix elements of I_z in (1.3). The perturbation operator is

$$H^1_{op} = -\gamma \hbar (H_x I_x + H_y I_y)$$
$$= -\tfrac{1}{2} \gamma \hbar H_1 \{(I_x - iI_y)e^{+i\omega t} + (I_x + iI_y)e^{-i\omega t}\} \qquad (1.12)$$

H^1_{op} has only non-diagonal elements, given by (1.1) and (1.2). In this problem one has to supply these two matrices with a Heisenberg time factor $e^{+i\omega_0 t}$ and $e^{-i\omega_0 t}$ respectively. The only effect of H^1_{op} is to produce transitions between adjacent levels. One has the selection rule $\triangle m_I = \pm 1$. Applying the usual first order perturbation theory one obtains for the probability to find the system in the state m' at time t, while at $t = 0$ it was in the state m:

$$w_{m \leftarrow m'} = \frac{1}{\hbar^2} \left| (m' | H^1 | m \right|^2 \left| \frac{1 - e^{i\triangle\omega t}}{\triangle\omega} \right|^2 \qquad (1.13)$$

where

$$\triangle\omega = \omega - \omega_0$$

Substituting (1.12) and (1.2) into (1.13) one finds:

$$w_{m+1 \leftarrow m} = \tfrac{1}{4}\gamma^2 H_1^2 (I - m)(I + m + 1)\sin^2\frac{\triangle\omega t}{2} / (\triangle\omega)^2 \quad (1.14)$$

This expression is very small, unless $\triangle\omega \approx 0$. Note that the resonance condition $\omega = \omega_0$ must also be satisfied to the sign in the complex phase factors $e^{\pm i\omega t}$. If the magnetogyric ratio is positive, H_1 must rotate counter clockwise, looking in the direction of H_0. Using the numerical value $\gamma \hbar I = 1.4 \times 10^{-23}$ E.M.U. for the moment of a proton, one finds that the resonance in a field of 6800 oersted occurs at 29 Mc/sec, that is, in the radio frequency range. If the radio frequency signal is spread out over a small frequency range containing the resonance frequency, and if we denote the average energy density stored in the rotating component of the magnetic field by $\int_0^\infty \varrho(\nu)\,d\nu = \dfrac{H_1^2}{8\pi}$ we have to integrate over $\triangle\omega$ in (1.14) and obtain in the familiar way a time proportional transition probability:

$$w_{m+1 \leftarrow m} = 2\pi\gamma^2 (I - m)(I + m + 1)\varrho(\nu_0)\,t \qquad (1.15)$$

If we assume that the chance to be in the initial state m is equal for all m's, we can average (1. 14) over m and obtain for the probability that any transition $\triangle m = +1$ is made

$$w_{\triangle m = +1} = \gamma^2 H_1^2 \, {}^2/_3 \, I (I + 1) \sin^2 \frac{\triangle \omega t}{2} / (\triangle \omega)^2$$

and (1. 15) goes over into;

$$w_{\triangle m = +1} = 2 \pi \gamma^2 \varrho (\nu_0) t \, {}^2/_3 \, I (I + 1) \qquad (1.16)$$

In the evaluation of the expression

$\dfrac{1}{2 I + 1} \sum\limits_{m = -I}^{+I} (I - m)(I + m + 1)$ the well known relations $\sum\limits_{m = -I}^{+I} m^2 =$

$= {}^1/_3 \, I \, (I + 1) \, (2 \, I + 1)$ and $\sum\limits_{m = -I}^{+I} m = 0$ have been used. The pro-

bability for a transition $\triangle m = -1$ is, of course, given by the same expression (1. 16), (1. 17). The probability per unit time for a transition of a spin $I = {}^1/_2$ from the parallel to the anti-parallel state is according to (1.15)

$$W = 2 \pi \gamma^2 \varrho (\nu_0) \qquad (1.17)$$

The resonance phenomenon is obviously just an „optical" magnetic dipole transition. The frequency, however, lies in the broadcast rather than the visible range.

1. 5. *The molecular beam magnetic resonance method.*

Gorter (G 4) was the first to point out how the phenomenon, described in the previous section, could be used to detect nuclear magnetism. The first successful experiment, however, was performed by Rabi (R 2) with his marvellous molecular beam technique.

Molecules evaporated from the furnace O, pass through some diaphragms to define a beam. The beam is split in the inhomogeneous field of magnet A, passed through a homogeneous field H_0 in magnet C, and is refocused onto a detector by an inhomogeneous field of magnet B, which deflects in the opposite direction as A. The refocusing condition is fulfilled only, if no reorientation of the nuclear spin occurs in magnet C. If a radio frequency magnetic field is applied, perpendicular to H_0, and either the radio frequency or H_0 is slowly changed, the current reaching the detector will pass through a minimum, when the resonance condition (1. 7) is fulfilled. Magnetogyric ratio's of many

Figure 1. 4.

Molecular beam magnetic resonance method, according to R a b i, M i l l m a n, K u s c h and Z a c h a r i a s, Phys. Rev. 55, 526, 1939.

Schematic representation of the paths of molecules in which the z-component of the magnetic moment of one of the nuclei has increased, decreased or remained unaltered in the region of magnet C.

nuclei have been measured in this way with great accuracy. The method is usually called the molecular beam method, although it can also be applied to atoms. A special and independent application to neutrons was made by B l o c h and A l v a r e z (A 2). For further information and literature the reader is referred to the review article by K e l l o g g and M i l l m a n (K 2).

1. 6. Nuclear Paramagnetism.

The permanent moments of the nuclei should be a source of paramagnetism. The theory of electronic paramagnetism (V 1) can be readily applied to nuclear moments, if one keeps in mind the similarity in the vector diagrams of $\vec{L}, \vec{S}$ and $\vec{J}$ and $\vec{J}, \vec{I}$ and $\vec{F}$. The contribution of the nuclei to the volume susceptibility is thus given by the well known L a n g e v i n formula

$$\chi_0 = N |\mu|^2 / 3 k T \tag{1.18}$$

where N is the number of nuclei per unit volume, and $|\mu|^2$ denotes the square of the absolute value of the magnetic moment

$$|\mu|^2 = \gamma^2 \hbar^2 I (I + 1) \tag{1.19}$$

Now it has to be borne in mind that the nuclear moments are about 10^8 times smaller than the electronic ones. Therefore nuclear susceptibilities are roughly a million times smaller than electronic ones. At room temperature the nuclear paramagnetic volume susceptibility of a solid would be of the order 10^{-9} erg / oersted^2, thus negligibly small compared to

✧✧

the ever present diamagnetic volume susceptibility of the order of 10^{-6} erg / oersted^2.

Only at very low temperatures might an influence of nuclear paramagnetism be detected. In the literature has been reported about one experiment which gives an indication for this effect. Shubnikoff (L 1) showed that the diamagnetic susceptibility of solid hydrogen decreased by 20%, when cooled down from 4.2° K to 1.7° K. This was attributed by him to an increase of the paramagnetic susceptibility of ortho-hydrogen. The paramagnetic susceptibility arising from the rotational magnetic moment of the molecules is only 3% of the nuclear paramagnetism. The experiment yields a value for the proton moment lying between 2.3 and 2.7 nuclear magnetons. It is to be noted that hydrogen with its few electrons (small diamagnetic effect) and its high density of protons with their relatively large nuclear moment is an exceptionally favorable case. For other substances still lower temperatures would be required. It is almost superfluous to note that saturation effects in nuclear magnetism would occur only at extremely low temperatures. The decisive quantity is $\gamma \hbar H_0/k\,T$, which at room temperature is 7.10^{-6} for protons in a field of 10^4 oersted. Therefore the Langevin formula (1. 18) should be valid down to about $0.01\,^\circ$K.

1. 7. *Nuclear magnetic resonance absorbtion and dispersion.*

Gorter (G 5) remarked that, just as e.g. in Na-vapor an anomalous electric dispersion occurs at the position of the yellow resonance line, there must be an anomaly in the nuclear paramagnetic susceptibility in the radio frequency range, if the substance is placed in a large magnetic field H_0. The anomalous dispersion, accompanied by an absorption, will occur at the frequency $\nu_0 = \gamma\,H_0/2\,\pi$.

The susceptibility will, roughly, increase by a factor $\nu_0/\triangle\nu = H_0/\triangle H$, where $\triangle\nu$ is the width of the resonance line. We shall see later that the line width is of the order of a few oersted or less. Therefore the volume susceptibility given by (1, 18) can be increased by a factor 10^4 at resonance or more and would there suddenly jump from practically zero to about 10^{-5}. In 1942 Gorter (G 5) attempted in vain to detect this change in susceptibility at low temperatures. The tank coil of an oscillator, filled with KF or LiCl powder, was placed in a field H_0. At the resonance of F^{19} and Li^7 a sudden change in the inductance of the coil should have produced an observable change in the oscillator frequency. Already six years earlier another unsuccesful attempt (G 4, G 6) has been made by the same author to detect the absorption by a resulting rise in temperature of the sample.

╈╈

21

The absorption can be described in the following way. In each transition from a level to the next higher one an energy $h\nu = \gamma \hbar H_0$ is absorbed by the nucleus, in the reverse process the nuclear spin system looses the same amount. The transition probability for absorption and stimulated emission is the same. But if the nuclear spin system is in thermal equilibrium there will be more nuclei in the states with lower energy. Thus there will be more transitions up than down, resulting in a net absorption.

We make the table

Level	Energy	Boltzmann factor
m_I	$-\gamma \hbar m_I H_0$	$exp\,(+\gamma \hbar m_I H_0 / kT)$

Since $h\nu = \gamma \hbar H_0 \ll kT.$ as we have seen in section 6, there is a constant difference n in population between two adjacent levels, which is small compared to the total number of nuclei N;

$$n = \frac{\gamma \hbar H_0}{kT} \frac{N}{2I+1} \qquad (1.20)$$

We have to multiply (1.15) by (1.20) to get the net surplus number of transitions up per second. If we then multiply by $h\nu$, we find for the absorbed power

$$P = {}^4/_3\, \pi\, \gamma^2\, \varrho\,(\nu_0)\,(\gamma \hbar H_0)^2\, N\, I(I+1)/kT \qquad (1.21)$$

The first positive effect of nuclear magnetic resonance absorption was obtained at the end of 1945 by Purcell, Torrey and Pound (P 7), soon afterwards, independently, by Bloch, Hansen and Packard (B 6). The resonance effect in the paramagnetic susceptibility is able to give at least as accurate information on nuclear moments as the molecular beam method. The most important new result for nuclear physics so far obtained with this new method is the magnetic moment and spin of H^3 (A 3, B 5), and the redetermination of the ratio of the moments of proton and neutron and proton and deuteron (A 4). The subject of the present thesis, however, is not to find resonances in a series of isotopes, but to investigate the interaction of the nuclei with one another and with other components of the surrounding substance.

For while in the beam method each particle can be considered as free, in the case of solids, liquids and gases the interaction between the nuclei and their surroundings cannot be neglected. They are, in fact, essential. If it were not for these interactions, the energy absorbed by the nuclei under the influence of a radio frequency magnetic field could not be dissipated and the temperature of the nuclear spin system, entirely isolated from the rest of the sample, would rise. The surplus number in the lower state would decrease, and soon the absorption and stimulated emission would be equal and in the stationary state no net absorption would take place. In the case $I = {}^1/_2$ the differential equation for the surplus number n would be

$$\frac{dn}{dt} = -2\,W\,n \tag{1.22}$$

with the solution

$$n = n\,(o)\,exp\,(-2\,Wt) \tag{1.23}$$

In this formula W is given by (1.17). The factor two is inserted, because in one transition the surplus number changes by two. With the relation (1.20) we find immediately that the temperature of the system of free spins would increase exponentially

$$T = T_{t=t_0}\,exp\,(+2\,Wt) \tag{1.24}$$

To avoid this heating up of the nuclear spin system, a process of energy dissipation must be taken into account. It will be shown in chapter 2 how the interaction between nuclei provides such a process by which thermal equilibrium is restored. The shape and the width of the resonance line will be shown to depend also on these interaction mechanisms, as one would expect. In chapter 3 the experimental method, developed by Purcell's group at Harvard University, will be described. In chapters 4 and 5 the theory will be applied to various substances and compared with experimental results obtained with nuclear resonances of H^1, H^2, Li^7 and F^{19} in these substances. It must be noted that actually a considerable part of the theory was developed after the experiments had been carried out, although sometimes the reverse was true. In order to present a readable account it proved necessary to deviate from the historical development in this thesis.

CHAPTER 2.

THEORY OF THE NUCLEAR MAGNETIC RESONANCE.

2. 1. *Rigorous classical solution for free spins.*

The description given in section 1. 4 of the transitions of a free spin in a rotating magnetic field needs some rectification. It is clear that, when in the classical picture the gyroscope has been turned over, the resonating field will start to turn it back, aud the result will be an oscillatory motion. The gyroscope will assume a nutation. The most convenient expression for the equation of motion of this problem is that the rate of change of angular momentum $\vec{J}$ equals the torque exerted by the magnetic field:

$$\frac{d\vec{J}}{dt} = [\vec{\mu} \times \vec{H}]$$

or with (1. 4):

$$\frac{d\vec{\mu}}{dt} = \gamma\, [\vec{\mu} \times \vec{H}] \qquad (2.\,1)$$

In a constant field $H_x = H_y = 0$, $H_z = H_0$ the solution of these equations is simply

$$
\begin{aligned}
\mu_x &= A \cos (\omega_0 t + \varphi) \\
\mu_y &= A \sin (\omega_0 t + \varphi) \\
\mu_z &= B
\end{aligned}
\qquad (2.\,2)
$$

with $\omega_0 = \gamma\, H_0$, and $A^2 + B^2 = \mu^2$. Classically tg $\vartheta = A/B$ can have any value. From quantummechanics we have the restriction that $\cos \vartheta = m_I / \sqrt{I(I+1)}$. If we have a large number of nuclei which combine to a large total quantumnumber I, the quantummechanical condition will not be severe and the total magnetic moment of the system of nuclei will be correctly described by (2. 1). T o r r e y showed that an exact solution can also be obtained for the rotating field (1. 6) by transforming to a coordinate system that rotates with the same angular velocity $\vec{\omega}$ as the magnetic field. The equations of motions in the new, primed system are (J 2):

$$\frac{D}{dt}\,\vec{\mu}' = \gamma[\mu' \times (\frac{\vec{\omega}}{\gamma} + \vec{H'})] \qquad (2.3)$$

where $\dfrac{D}{dt}$ denotes differentiation with respect to time in the moving system. In the primed system the magnetic field is constant $H_x' = H_1$, $H_y' = 0$, $H_z' = H_0$.

So $\vec{\mu}'$ will precess about the fixed vector $+ \vec{H'} - \vec{\omega}/\gamma$ according to equation (2. 1) with an angular velocity

$$\lambda = \sqrt{(\pm \omega + \gamma H_0)^2 + \gamma^2 H_1{}^2} = \sqrt{(\pm \omega + \omega_0)^2 + \omega_1{}^2} \qquad (2.4)$$

In this formula the sign of ω is positive if $\vec{\omega}$ points in the same direction as $\vec{H_0}$. At resonance $\omega = \omega_0$.

The precession becomes a nutation in the original system. We can impose various initial conditions on the general solution of the differential equation. If at $t = 0$ the moment $\vec{\mu}$ is parallel to the vector $\vec{H'} - \vec{\omega}/\gamma$, there is no nutation. In this case we have a pure rotation in the resting system with an angle ϑ given by

$$tg\,\vartheta = \frac{H_1}{-\omega/\gamma + H_0} = \frac{\omega_1}{-\omega + \omega_0} \qquad (2.5)$$

At resonance we have $\vartheta = \pi/2$. If we start with a constant field $H_z = H_0$ and $\vec{\mu}$ aligned in the z-direction, and at $t = 0$ suddenly apply a rotating component H_1, the moment $\vec{\mu}$ will start to precess with an angular velocity λ and angle $\vartheta = \text{arc } tg\ \omega_1/(\omega_0 - \omega)$. Then it follows from simple geometrical considerations, that the z-component of $\vec{\mu}$ as a function of time in the original system is given by

$$\mu_z = \mu \cos^2 \vartheta + \mu \sin^2 \vartheta \cos \lambda t$$
$$\mu_z = \mu (1 - 2 \sin^2 \vartheta \sin^2 {}^1/_2 \lambda t) \qquad (2.6)$$

2. 2. *Rigorous quantummechanical solution for free spins.*

The quantummechanical solution (1. 14) also needs some revision. The application of perturbation theory is only valid for a short period of time, at the end of which the probability of finding the system in the original state is still of the order of unity. In other words (1. 14) holds only as long as $w \ll 1$. An exact solution valid for any time t has been given by Rabi (R 1) in the case $I = \frac{1}{2}$. The problem is to solve the time dependent Schrödinger equation

$$H_{op} \psi(t) = \frac{\hbar}{i} \frac{\partial \psi(t)}{\partial t} \qquad (2.7)$$

where the Hamiltonian H_{op} is given by (1. 9), and the wave function $\psi(t)$ has two components

$$\psi(t) = c_{1/2}(t) \, \psi_{1/2} + c_{-1/2}(t) \, \psi_{-1/2} \qquad (2.8)$$

The normalised spin wave functions $\psi_{1/2}$ and $\psi_{-1/2}$ belong to the eigenvalues $m_I = \frac{1}{2}$ and $m_I = -\frac{1}{2}$; $| c_{1/2}(t) |^2$ and $| c_{-1/2}(t) |^2$ are the probabilities to find the system at time t in the state $m_I = +\frac{1}{2}$ or $m_I = -\frac{1}{2}$ respectively. Since the system must be in one state or another, we have the normalisation condition

$$| c_{1/2}(t) |^2 + | c_{-1/2}(t) |^2 = 1 \qquad (2.9)$$

Equation (2. 7) can be written in matrix form

$$\frac{\hbar}{i} \begin{pmatrix} \dot{c}_{1/2} \\ \dot{c}_{-1/2} \end{pmatrix} = -\gamma \hbar \begin{pmatrix} H_0 & H_x + iH_y \\ H_x - iH_y & H_0 \end{pmatrix} \begin{pmatrix} c_{1/2} \\ c_{-1/2} \end{pmatrix} \qquad (2.10)$$

These two simultaneous differential equations can be solved with the initial conditon $| c_{1/2}(t) |^2 = 1$ at $t = 0$.

Rabi finds for the probability that the system is in the state $m_I = -\frac{1}{2}$ at time t

$$| c_{-1/2}(t) |^2 = w_{-1/2, 1/2} = \frac{\omega_1^2}{(\omega - \omega_0)^2 + \omega_1^2} \sin^2 \frac{t}{2} \sqrt{(\omega - \omega_0)^2 + \omega_1^2} \qquad (2.11)$$

This correspondends exactly to the classical solution (2. 6), if one remembers that for spin $\frac{1}{2}$, $\mu_z = \mu(1 - 2 w_{-1/2, 1/2})$.

Schwinger (S 3) showed that for obtaining the quantummechanical solution it also has some advantage to transform to a rotating coordinate system. The results can be extended to the case of arbitrary spin by the general M a j o r a n a formula, which one can find in R a b i's paper (R 1, B 8). We note that (2. 11) goes over into (1. 14) for very small values of the perturbation field $\omega_1 \ll \omega - \omega_0$. At resonance $\omega = \omega_0$, $w_{-1/2, \, 1/2}$ becomes equal to unity for $t = \pi/\omega_1$. The system then oscillates between the states with spin parallel and antiparallel to the magnetic field. If $\omega \neq \omega_0$, the system never attains the pure state with $m = -1/2$, and oscillates more rapidly than at resonance for the same value of H_1. We can define the width of the resonance curve as the distance between the points, where the maximum chance to find the system in the antiparallel state is one half. From (2. 11) we see that $|\omega - \omega_0| = \omega_1$ for those points, or the width measured in oersted is twice the amplitude of the radiofrequency field. The energy of the spin system in the magnetic field H_0 (at $t = 0$, all n spins are parallel to the field) is given by

$$E(t) = -1/2 \, (1 - 2 \, w) \, \gamma \, \hbar \, H_0 \, n \qquad (2.12)$$

and the time derivative of this expression yields the absorbed power, which behaves as $\sin t \, \sqrt{(\omega - \omega_0)^2 + \omega_1^2}$. In the average no net absorption of energy takes place. Suppose now that we have an assembly of free spins in a not perfectly homogeneous magnetic field. The distribution function of the spins over the resonance frequencies be $\varphi(\nu)$ which is normalised $\int_0^\infty \varphi(\nu) \, d\nu = 1$. We assume that the distribution over the inhomogeneous field is much wider than the width of the resonance, which, expressed in oersted, is about H_1. We assume that $\varphi(\nu)$ is practically constant near the resonance $\varphi(\nu) \approx \varphi(\nu_0)$ for $|\nu - \nu_0| < \nu_1$. Then the energy absorbed by the system is

$$E(t) = \int_0^\infty w_{-1/2, \, 1/2} (\nu) \, \gamma \, \hbar \, H_0 \, n \, \varphi(\nu) \, d\nu =$$

$$= \frac{1}{2\pi} \, \gamma \, \hbar \, H_0 \, \varphi(\nu_0) \, n \int_0^\infty \frac{\omega_1^2 \sin^2 \frac{t}{2} \sqrt{(\omega - \omega_0^1)^2 + \omega_1^2}}{(\omega - \omega_0^1)^2 + \omega_1^2} \, d\omega_0^1 \quad (2.13)$$

Take the time derivative, representing the power absorbed, of this expression. The integral can then be evaluated in terms of the Bessel function of zero order.

$$\frac{dE(t)}{dt} = P(t) = 1/4 \, \omega_1^2 \, \gamma \, \hbar \, H_0 \, \varphi(\nu_0) \, n \, J_0(\gamma \, H_1 \, t) \qquad (2.15)$$

For small t we find, substituting $J_0(0) = 1$, in (2. 15)

$$P(t) = \frac{1}{4} \gamma^2 H_1^2 \varphi(\nu_0) n \gamma \hbar H_0 \qquad (2.16)$$

It is not surprising that this comes out to be the same as if we had used a time proportional transition probability given by (1.17) to calculate the absorbed power.

In the derivation of that formula we had supposed a range of frequencies in the radio frequency signal, over which we had to integrate, as is usually done in optics. In the case of a single applied frequency, but a distribution over H_0, we have to integrate rather over a range of resonance frequencies. Since ω and ω_0 occur only in the combination $\omega - \omega_0$, the result is the same. In r.f. spectra this last case is more common, quite contrary to the situation usually encountered in optics. From (2.15) we see that in the stationary state here is again no net absorption of energy as the Bessel function vanishes as $x^{-1/2}$ for large arguments. This means that the free spins, initially all oriented in one direction, start oscillating under the influence of the applied signal, get out of phase and for large t there are always as many pointing up as down.

2.3. Interaction with radiation.

In order to keep an absorption in the stationary state, it is necessary that there is some mechanism trying to restore thermal equilibrium so that the population of the spin levels does not become equal. The time T_1, it takes for the spin system to come back to thermal equilibrium, after this has been disturbed some way or other, e.g. by a large radio frequency signal at resonance, is called the relaxation time. The experiments described in chapter 3 and 4 yield values for the relaxation time, ranging from 10^{-4} to 10^2 seconds. We shall now discuss some interaction mechanisms which tend to restore thermal equilibrium. Even for the so called „free" particles one always has the interaction with radiation. The spontaneous emission which usually limits the life time for an atom in a electronically excited state to 10^{-8} sec, is negligibly small for radio frequency transitions. The coefficient for spontaneous emission A of dipole radiation (H 1) is proportional to the cube of the frequency and the square of the dipole moment.

$$A = 8 \pi h \nu^3 B/c^3 \qquad (2.17)$$

where B is the coefficient of absorption or induced emission, i.e. w in (1.15), is $\varrho(\nu_0)$ and t are taken to be unity. Substituting numerical values for protons in a field of 10^4 oersted one finds $A = 10^{-25}$ sec^{-1}, corresponding to a life time of 10^{19} years. This is not the relaxation time caused by the radiative interaction. For, in addition to the spontaneous emission, we have the transitions induced by the thermal radiation field. Take $I = \frac{1}{2}$, and let n^+ and n^- denote the number of spins in the upper and lower level respectively, n^+ satisfies the differential equation

$$\frac{dn^+}{dt} = B\varrho(\nu) n^- - \{A + B\varrho(\nu)\} n^+ \tag{2.18}$$

Using $n^+ + n^- = N$ we find

$$n^+ = C e^{-\{A + 2B\varrho(\nu)\} t} + \frac{B\varrho(\nu)}{A + 2B\varrho(\nu)} N \tag{2.19}$$

Thus the relaxation time T_1, if radiation were the only interaction, would be $\{A + 2B\varrho(\nu)\}^{-1}$. Here $\varrho(\nu)$ is the energy density of the electromagnetic field. As for the nuclear resonance $h\nu/kT \ll 1$, we may use Rayleigh's approximation

$$\varrho(\nu) = 8\pi\nu^2 kT c^{-3} \tag{2.20}$$

With $B = 2\pi\gamma^2$, we find $T_1 \approx 10^{13}$ years. Although the influence of the thermal radiation field is much larger than that of the spontaneous emission at these low frequencies, the effect of the radiation is far too small to play any role in the explanation of the observed relaxation times. Purcell (P 4) pointed out that the energy density of blackbody radiation is not given by Rayleigh's formula, if the wave length is large compared to the dimensions of the black body. This is exactly the case at radio frequences in a tuned LC circuit. The energy density at the resonance frequency is increased, because the energy kT of the circuit is stored in a narrow frequency range.

The mean square voltage across a resistor of temperature T is $\overline{V^2} = 4RkT\triangle\nu$.

At resonance the current is

$$\overline{i^2} = 4kT\triangle\nu/R$$

Figure 2.1.
Noise in a tuned circuit.

The energy stored in the coil is $\frac{1}{2}L\overline{i^2}$. Introduce $Q = \omega L/R$ and the volume of the coil V. We find for the energy density of the supposedly homogeneous magnetic field per unit frequency range

$$\varrho(\nu) = kTQ/\pi\nu V \tag{2.21}$$

The increase over the energy density in a large black-body cavity is given by the factor $\lambda^3\, Q/8\,\pi^2\, V$. Substituting $V = 1$ cc, $\lambda = 10^8$ cm, $Q = 100$, we find that the relaxation time is decreased by a factor 10^9, but is still 10^8 years, so several orders of magnitude above the experimental values.

2. 4. Dipole — dipole interaction.

Looking for other types of interaction besides the very small radiation damping, the contact of the nuclear spin system with the outside world appears to be very limited. Electric forces, which act during atomic and electronic collisions and play e.g. an important role in the mechanism of arcs, readily establish an equilibrium for electronic states. But they do not perturb the nuclear spin. Only a gradient of an electric field can interact with a nuclear quadrupole moment, as will be considered in chapter 5.

We shall neglect the possibility of interaction by exchange forces. For electronic states with overlapping wave functions this exchange is sometimes considerable (ferromagnetism or antiferromagnetism). But for the nuclei in crystals and liquids at room temperature exchange is not likely to occur.

So we come back to a magnetic type of interaction, by means of the magnetic moment associated with the nuclear spin. This interaction will of course, be much smaller than the corresponding magnetic interaction of electronic moments, as the nuclear magneton is so much smaller than the Bohr magneton. So far the magnetic field acting on a nucleus was taken to consist only of the externally applied field $H_0 + H_1$ and the thermal radiation field. Every nucleus, however, also experiences the field produced by the magnetic moments of its neighbours. If this dipole — dipole interaction is taken into account, the Hamiltonian (1.9) for an assembly of spins becomes

$$H_{op} = \Sigma_i\, \gamma_i\, \hbar \vec{I}_i \cdot \vec{H}_0 + \Sigma_i\, \gamma_i\, \hbar \vec{I}_i \cdot \Sigma_j \left(\frac{\gamma_j\, \hbar \vec{I}_j}{r^3_{ij}} - \frac{3\gamma_j\, \hbar \vec{r}_{ij}(\vec{r}_{ij} \cdot \vec{I}_j)}{r^5_{ij}} \right) \quad (2.24)$$

The sum over j in the right hand term represents the internal or local field H_{loc} at the ith nucleus; $\vec{r}_{ij} = \vec{r}_j - \vec{r}_i$ is the radiusvector connecting the ith and the jth spin. The problem connected with (2.24) is one of an extreme complexity. It is the equation of motion for N particles, where N is of the order of the number of Avogadro. The local field will, at any time, be of the order of few oersted. It is mainly determined by the nearest neighbours, since the magnitude of a dipole field decreases as the inverse cube of the distance: $H_{loc} \approx \gamma \hbar / a^3$ where a is the internuclear distance. For two protons, one Ångstrøm apart, we find $H_{loc} \approx 10$ oersted, The problem (2. 24) of an assembly of spins also comes up in the theory of the absorption and dispersion of electronic magnetism in paramagnetic salts. Gorter (G 3) gives a survey of experiment and theory in this field. The reader will find in this book ample references to the existing literature. Using the classification customary in electronic magnetism, the case which is of interest here is that of no electric splitting and a strong transverse field. It must be stressed that we are interested in a resonance absorption. Recently the first experiments of electronic magnetic resonance at microwave frequencies have been reported (C 6). Most of the work on absorption and dispersion in paramagnetic crystals, however, relates to the non-resonant absorption. We shall here proceed on similar lines as Broer (B 12).

The energy levels of the unperturbed system, without dipole-dipole interaction are (compare (2. 12))

$$E_n = \tfrac{1}{2}\, n\, \gamma\, \hbar\, H_0 \qquad (2.\,25)$$

If $I = \tfrac{1}{2}$, $n = N^+ - N^-$ is the difference between the number of spins which are parallel or antiparallel to H_0. Since n is even or odd, depending on whether the total number $N = N^+ + N^-$ is even or odd, the spacing between the equidistant levels is $\gamma \hbar H_0$. The degeneracy of the levels is high, $N!/N^+!\,N^-!$, but is lifted by the interaction term in (2. 24). Now the perturbation energy will be of the order $N^{1/2} \gamma \hbar H_{loc}$. Although $H_{loc} \ll H_0$, the perturbation energy for an assembly of many

Figure 2. 2.

The distribution D of energy levels of a spin system in a magnetic field H_0 and the distribution of occupied states ϱ, obtained by multiplying D with the Bolzmann factor $e^{-H_{op}/kT}$. Both functions are normalised.

spins ($N \approx 10^{22}$) will be large compared to the spacing of the unperturbed levels. In view of the large number of non-degenerate levels we can say that the energy levels belonging to (2. 24) are spread over a continuum. The density D of the energy levels as a function of the energy has sharp maximum, the width being of the order $N^{1/2} \gamma \hbar H_0$. The average occupation ϱ of the continuum is obtained by multiplying D by the Bolzmann factor $\exp(-H_{op}/k T)$. The regular spacing $\gamma \hbar H_0$ has completely vanished from the picture. It seems as if the whole resonance phenomenon disappeared, for one might expect transitions from any level p to any level q in the continuous distribution, when a rotating magnetic field H_1 is applied with frequency $\nu = E_p - E_q /h$. The probability for such a process per unit time is

$$
\begin{aligned}
W_{q \leftarrow p} &= {}^{1}/_{4} \gamma^2 H_1{}^2 \mid (p \mid \sum_j (I_x + i I_y)_j \mid q) \mid^2 \varrho_q \\
&= \frac{1}{4 \hbar^2} H_1{}^2 \mid M_{pq} \mid^2 \varrho_q
\end{aligned}
\tag{2. 26}
$$

where M_{pq} is the matrix element of the rotating component of the total magnetic moment between the states p and q. The absorbed power $P(\nu)$ is obtained by subtracting from (2. 26) the transitions from q to p, multiplying by the involved energy $h \nu$ and summing over a small frequency interval $2 \triangle \nu$ around ν. For $h \nu/k T \ll 1$ we can write

$$
\varrho_p - \varrho_q = \varrho_{pq} \, h \, \nu/k \, T
\tag{2. 27}
$$

with $\varrho_{pq} \approx (\varrho_p + \varrho_q)/2$

$$
P(\nu) = \frac{H_1{}^2}{4 \hbar^2} \frac{h^2 \nu^2}{k T} \sum_{\nu - \triangle \nu}^{\nu + \triangle \nu} \left| M_{pq} \right|^2 \varrho_{pq}
$$

Introducing the absorption coefficient $A(\nu) = \dfrac{P(\nu) 16 \pi}{H_1{}^2}$ and the density function of the magnetic moment

$$
f(\nu) = 2 \sum_{\nu - \triangle \nu}^{\nu + \triangle \nu} \left| M_{pq} \right|^2 \varrho_{pq}
\tag{2. 28}
$$

we find

$$
A(\nu) = \frac{8 \pi^3 \nu^2}{k T} f(\nu)
\tag{2. 29}
$$

These last two equations are identical with those of Broer (Thesis,

p. 63). The problem is reduced to determining $f(\nu)$. The only exact way for solving this problem is the diagonal sum method, developed by Waller, Van Vleck and Broer (W 1, V 2, B 13). Neglecting terms in $h\nu/kT$, they find the relations

$$\int_0^\infty f(\nu)\, d\nu = \text{Spur } M^2$$

$$\int_0^\infty \nu^2 f(\nu)\, d\nu = \text{Spur } \dot{M}^2/4\,\pi^2$$

$$\int_0^\infty \nu^4 f(\nu)\, d\nu = \text{Spur } \ddot{M}^2/16\,\pi^4 \quad \text{etc.} \tag{2.30}$$

Furthermore we have the general relation for the time derivative of a quantummechanical operator

$$i\,\hbar\,\dot{M} = HM - MH \tag{2.31}$$

where H is the Hamiltonian.

The mean square frequency of the absorption curve $A(\nu)$ is the quotient of the first two expressions (2.30)

$$\overline{\nu^2} = \frac{\text{Spur}\,(HM - MH)^2}{h^2 \text{ Spur } M^2} \tag{2.32}$$

The shape of the curve remains obscure. Strictly speaking, one does not even know whether there is a resonance at all. Unfortunately the the quantities $\overline{\nu^4}$, $\overline{\nu^6}$ etc. are hard to calculate, although in principle they will give more information about the shape of the absorption curve (V 3).

Our knowledge is supplemented by the perturbation method. At first it may seem strange that a perturbation theory can be applied, since we have seen that the perturbation energy is larger than the spacing of the unperturbed levels. However, as Broer pointed out, the matrix elements of the magnetic moment operator differ appreciably from zero only when the energy difference $h\triangle\nu$ between two states p and q satisfies the relation $h\triangle\nu \approx \gamma\,\hbar\,H_{loc}$ or $h\triangle\nu \approx \gamma\,\hbar(H_0 \pm H_{loc})$ or $h\triangle\nu \approx \gamma\,\hbar\,(2\,H_0 \pm H_{loc})$.

The schematic behaviour of $f(\nu)$ is plotted in fig. 2.3. The absorption can be obtained from (2.29). The absorption at the Larmor frequency is a first order effect, in which we are interested. The absorption near a frequency of zero or $2\,\nu$ is of the order $(H_{loc}/H_0)^2$ and so about 10^6 times smaller than at ν_0, and unobservable in the case of nuclear magnetism.

The use of the perturbation theory is justified by its results, which

33

Figure 2. 3.

The density function $f(v)$ of the magnetic moment (cf. Broer, B 12).

are in agreement with the experimental facts, one of which is the occurrence of a sharp resonance at the frequency v_0. The perturbation method gives more details than the diagonal sum method, but is less rigorous and certain. Sometimes it is advantageous to combine them.

The unperturbed state of the system is specified by the quantumnumbers m_{I_j} of all spins, the total z-component of the spins being $m = \sum_j m_j$. We assume that these magnetic quantum numbers still characterize a state after the introduction of the perturbation

$$V = \sum_{j > i} \sum V_{ij}$$

$$V_{ij} = \frac{\gamma^2 \hbar^2}{r^3_{ij}} [I_{x_i} I_{x_j} (1 - 3\,a_1^2) + I_{y_i} I_{y_j} (1 - 3\,a_2^2) + I_{z_i} I_{z_j} (1 - 3\,a_3^2) - \\ - 3 (I_{x_i} I_{y_j} + I_{x_j} I_{y_i})\, a_1\, a_2 - 3 (I_{x_i} I_{z_j} + I_{x_j} I_{z_i})\, a_1\, a_3 - \\ - 3 (I_{y_i} I_{z_j} + I_{y_j} I_{z_i})\, a_2\, a_3]$$

(2. 33)

V_{ij} is the magnetic interaction between the ith and j^{th} spin; a_1, a_2 and a_3 are the direction cosines of the radius vector $\vec{r}_{ij}$ with respect to a system, of which the z-axis is parallel to H_0. We shall now write the operator (2. 33) in the m-representation, so that we can distinguish terms which leave the total z-component m unchanged, $\triangle m = 0$, and terms for which $\triangle m = +1$ or -1 and those for which $\triangle m = +2$ or -2. The elements with $\triangle m = 0$ leave the energy unchanged. With off-diagonal elements is a change in energy $\triangle m \gamma \hbar H_0$ connected. We make use of the relations

$$I_{x_i} I_{x_j} + I_{y_i} I_{y_j} = \frac{(I_{x_i} - i I_{y_i})(I_{x_j} + i I_{y_j})}{2} + \frac{(I_{x_i} + i I_{y_i})(I_{x_j} - i I_{y_j})}{2}$$

$$I_{x_i} I_{x_j} - I_{y_i} I_{y_j} = \frac{(I_{x_i} + i I_{y_i})(I_{x_j} + i I_{y_j})}{2} + \frac{(I_{x_i} - i I_{y_i})(I_{x_j} - i I_{y_j})}{2}$$

$$I_{x_i} I_{y_j} + I_{x_j} I_{y_i} = \frac{(I_{x_i} + i I_{y_i})(I_{x_j} + i I_{y_j})}{2 i} - \frac{(I_{x_i} - i I_{y_i})(I_{x_j} - i I_{y_j})}{2 i}$$

$$I_{x_i} I_{z_j} = \tfrac{1}{2}(I_{x_i} + i I_{y_i}) I_{z_j} + \tfrac{1}{2}(I_{x_i} - i I_{y_i}) I_{z_j}$$

$$I_{y_i} I_{z_j} = \frac{1}{2 i}(I_{x_i} + i I_{y_i}) I_{z_j} - \frac{1}{2 i}(I_{x_i} - i I_{y_i}) I_{z_j}$$

and introduce the polar and azimuthal angles ϑ_{ij}, and φ_{ij}, instead of the direction cosines. We can then write (2.33) in the form, adding the Heisenberg time factors $\exp(i \triangle m \gamma H t)$,

$$V_{ij} = \frac{\gamma^2 \hbar^2}{r^3_{ij}} (A + B + C + D + E + F) \qquad (2.34)$$

$\triangle m = 0$
$$A = I_{z_i} I_{z_j} (1 - 3 \cos^2 \vartheta_{ij})$$

$\triangle m = 0$
$$B = -\tfrac{1}{4}\{(I_{x_i} - i I_{y_i})(I_{x_j} + i I_{y_j}) + \\ + (I_{x_i} + i I_{y_i})(I_{x_j} - i I_{y_j})\}(1 - 3 \cos^2 \vartheta_{ij})$$

$\triangle m = 1$
$$C = -\tfrac{3}{2}\{(I_{x_i} + i I_{y_i}) I_{z_j} + \\ + (I_{x_j} + i I_{y_j}) I_{z_i}\} \sin \vartheta_{ij} \cos \vartheta_{ij} e^{-i \varphi_{ij}} e^{i \gamma H_0 t}$$

$\triangle m = -1$
$$D = -\tfrac{3}{2}\{(I_{x_i} - i I_{y_i}) I_{z_j} + \\ + (I_{x_j} - i I_{y_j}) I_{z_i}\} \sin \vartheta_{ij} \cos \vartheta_{ij} e^{+i \varphi_{ij}} e^{-i \gamma H_0 t}$$

$\triangle m = 2$
$$E = \tfrac{3}{4}(I_{x_i} + i I_{y_i})(I_{x_j} + i I_{y_j}) \sin^2 \vartheta_{ij} e^{-2 i \varphi_{ij}} e^{2 i \gamma H_0 t}$$

$\triangle m = -2$
$$F = \tfrac{3}{4}(I_{x_i} - i I_{y_i})(I_{x_j} - i I_{y_j}) \sin^2 \vartheta_{ij} e^{+2 i \varphi_{ij}} e^{-2 i \gamma H_0 t}$$

The first two terms give rise to secular perturbations, the last four are periodical perturbations of very small amplitudes. K r a m e r s gives a clear exposition of these two different types of perturbation in his book on quantum mechanics (K 6). That the terms C to F cannot give rise to appreciable changes also follows from the principle of conservation of energy. So we keep only the terms A and B. Classically A corresponds to the change in the z-component of the magnetic field by the z-component of the neighbouring nuclear moments. This local field will vary from nucleus to nucleus, slightly changing the Larmor frequency of each. Let us consider in somewhat more detail the situation at the ith nucleus. Let us suppose for simplicity that the neighbouring nuclei have spin $I = \frac{1}{2}$. Each of them can be parallel or antiparallel to H_0. For each configuration we have a definite value of the z-component of the local field. Let us first consider only the nearest neighbours. Instead of one value H_0, we have e.g. ten possible values around H_0, depending which neighbours are parallel and which antiparallel to H_0. Now all the configurations of the next nearest neighbours will split each of the ten values into many more, and so on for the third nearest, etc. The result will be a continuum of values of the z-component of the local field and therefore a distribution over a range of Larmor frequencies. In many cases this distribution, approximately will have a Gaussian shape, as was pointed out by several authors (K 10, V 2). But we want to stress that this is not necessarily so. Take for instance the case of a substance in which the nuclei occur in pairs. That is, each nucleus has one very close neighbour, while the next nearest are relatively far away. The nearest neighbour will split the H_0 value into two discrete values, rather far apart. The next nearest neighbours will produce a bell shaped distribution of the Larmor frequency around each of these two discrete values. The nuclear resonance line will show a fine structure in this case. This has been observed experimentally in many crystals by P a k e (P 1). It will be very difficult to obtain information about the fine structure with the diagonal sum method.

So we see that for each crystal a detailed investigation would be required. But as in many cases the line will be a Gaussian anyway, we can obtain an estimate of the line width by calculating the mean square contribution of each nucleus separately, and taking the square root of the sum of these contributions, as the orientation of each nucleus is independent of the others. The mean square local field from term A is given by

$$\overline{(\Delta H_{loc})^2} = \gamma^2 \hbar^2 \frac{I(I+1)}{3} \sum_j \frac{(1 - 3\cos^2 \vartheta_{ij})^2}{r^6_{ij}} \qquad (2.35)$$

and the mean square deviation in frequency by

$$\overline{(\triangle \omega)^2} = \gamma^2 \, \overline{(\triangle H_{loc})^2}.$$

To this we have to add the contribution of term B. To B corresponds the simultaneous flopping of two antiparallel spins ($\triangle m_i = + 1$ and $\triangle m_j = - 1$ or vice versa). This process is energetically possible and is caused by the precession of the nuclei around H_0 with the Larmor frequency. So they produce an oscillating field of resonance frequency at the position of their neighbours, resulting in reciprocal transitions. Classically one might say that this process limits the life time of the spin in a given state and therefore broadens the spectrum. To (2. 35) we have to add a numerical factor to take the effect of B into account.

The proper factor has been calculated by Van Vleck (V 3) in a rigorous manner with the diagonal sum method, using formula (2. 32). For H_{op} we take the terms of type A and B of the perturbation $\underset{j > i}{\Sigma \Sigma} V_{ij}$. The component of the magnetic moment, rotating with the applied radio frequency field, is proportional to $\underset{j}{\Sigma} I_{x_j} + i I_{y_j}$. We can evaluate the commutator by making use of the commutation rules which exist for the components of the angular momentum operator I. Van Vleck's (V 3) result is

$$(1/T_2')_{asymptotic} \equiv \sqrt{\overline{(\triangle \omega)^2}} = {}^3/_2 \, \gamma^2 \, \hbar \, \sqrt{\frac{I(I+1)}{3}} \sqrt{\underset{j}{\Sigma} \frac{(1 - 3 \cos^2 \vartheta_{ij})^2}{r^6_{ij}}} \quad (2.36)$$

This formula, valid for a system of identical spins, holds for any shape of the nuclear resonance line. We have no information what the contribution to $\sqrt{\overline{(\triangle \omega)^2}}$ from the tails is. For a Gaussian $(2/T_2')_{asymptotic}$ is the width between the points of maximum slope. The reason for this notation we shall see later.

2.5. The relaxation time.

So far we still have not found a relaxation process. For we argued that only processes with $\triangle m = 0$ can occur. To restore thermal equilibrium it is essential that the energy of the spin system changes. We have tacitly assumed that the position coordinates r_{ij}, ϑ_{ij} and φ_{ij} are constants, and we have seen that the dipole-dipole interaction of nuclei at fixed positions only gives a broadening of the levels. Now we shall show that energy transfer is produced, if *the position vectors $\overrightarrow{r_{ij}}$ are functions of the time* (B 11). This is the only new feature in the treatment of the spin system presented here. In practice the nuclei will always move to some extent, if the system has not zero temperature. In a crystal we have the lattice vibrations, while in a liquid or gas we have the Brownian movement. As far as the Hamiltonian (2.24) for the nuclei is concerned, we can consider this motion of the molecules as to be produced by external forces, since the atomic interactions are mainly of electric nature. In doing so we neglect, of course, the reaction of the magnetic moment of the nuclei on the Brownian motion. We expand the factors in (2.34), which contain the position coordinates and are thus functions of the time, into a series of Fourier or better a Fourier integral. We want to distingiush in our complex notation between positive and negative frequencies and we therefore define the intensity $J(\nu)$ of the Fourier spectra of the functions of the position coordinates

$$F_0 = \sum_{ij} (1 - 3\cos^2 \vartheta_{ij}) / r^3_{ij}$$

$$F_1 = \sum_{ij} \sin \vartheta_{ij} \cos \vartheta_{ij} \; e^{i \, \varphi_{ij}} / r^3_{ij}$$

$$F_2 = \sum_{ij} \sin^2 \vartheta_{ij} \; e^{2i \, \varphi_i} / r^3_{ij}$$

by the equations *):

$$\overline{\sum_j \left| (1 - 3\cos^2 \vartheta_{ij}(t)) \Big/ r^3_{ij}(t) \right|^2} = \int_{-\infty}^{+\infty} J_0(\nu) \, d(\nu) \qquad (2.37)$$

$$\overline{\sum_j \left| \sin \vartheta_{ij}(t) \cos \vartheta_{ij}(t) \, e^{i \, \varphi_{ij}(t)} \Big/ r^3_{ij}(t) \right|^2} = \int_{-\infty}^{+\infty} J_1 \, \nu \, d(\nu) \quad (2.38)$$

$$\overline{\sum_j \left| \sin^2 \vartheta_{ij}(t) \, e^{2i \, \varphi_{ij}(t)} \Big/ r^3_{ij}(t) \right|^2} = \int_{-\infty}^{+\infty} J_2(\nu) \, d\nu \qquad (2.39)$$

We shall first reconsider the terms C, D, E and F in the expression (2.34) for the perturbation. If $J_2(2\nu_0)$ and $J_2(-2\nu_0)$ are different from zero, E and F become secular perturbation, because the time factor cancels out. Similary C and D become secular perturbations, if $J_1(\nu_0)$

---

*) In section 4.1 the reader will find a short discussion of the Fourier series and spectral intensity of a random function.

and J_1 $(-\nu_0)$ do not vanish. The action of the terms C and D may classically be described as transitions induced by the Larmor frequency of the spectrum of the local field. The thermal motion provides the energy necessary for the change $\triangle m$. The interaction of the nuclei with the thermal motion is the relaxation mechanism. From E and F we see, that, quantum-mechanically the simultaneous transition of two nuclei is also a possible process. Let us ask for the probability for a change $\triangle m_i = +1$ in the magnetic quantumnumber of the ith spin. We repeat the simple perturbation calculation of chapter 1 with the terms C and E rather than (1.12): Taking the average over all values m_j of the neighbours we find for the transition probability,

$$W_{m_i+1 \,\leftarrow\, m_i} = {}^9/_{16}\, \gamma^4\, \hbar^2\, J_2\, (-2\,\nu_0)\, {}^2/_3\, I\, (I+1)\, (I-m_i)\, (I+m_i+1) +$$
$$+ {}^9/_4\, \gamma^4\, \hbar^2 J_1\, (-\nu_0)\, {}^1/_3\, I\, (I+1)\, (I-m_i)\, (I+m_i+1) \quad (2.40)$$

It is simple to generalize (2.40) to the case that the spins and magnetogyric ratio's of the nuclei are not all the same

$$W_{m_i+1 \,\leftarrow\, m_i} = {}^3/_8\, \gamma_i^2\hbar^2(I-m_i)(I_i+m_i+1)\,\underset{j}{\varSigma}\, [J_{2j}\, (-\nu_{o_i}-\nu_{o_j}) +$$
$$+ 2\, J_{1j}\, (-\nu_{o_i})] \quad (2.41)$$

where $J_{2\,j}$ stands for the intensity of

$$\gamma_j\, \sqrt{I_j(I_j+1)}\, \sin^2\vartheta_{ij}\, e^{2\,\varphi_{ij}}/\, r^3{}_{ij}.$$

The neighbouring moments may now also be caused by molecular rotation or they may consist of electronic spins and orbital momenta. In these cases not only the position coordinates may be a function of the time, but also the quantisation of the spin $m_j\,(t)$ must be regarded as time dependent under the influence of external forces. Instead of (2.41) we should write

$$W_{m_i+1 \,\leftarrow\, m} = \gamma_i{}^2\hbar^2(I_i-m_i)(I_i+m_i+1)\, [J''\, (-\nu_{o_j}-\nu_{o_i}) + J'\, (-\nu_{o_i})] \quad (2.42)$$

where $J''\, (\nu)$ is the intensity of the function

$$\underset{j}{\varSigma}\Big[\sqrt{{}^3/_8\, [\, I_j-m_j(t)\,][\, I_j+m_j(t)+1\,]}\, \sin^2\vartheta_{ij}(t)\, e^{2\,i\,\varphi_{ij}\,(t)}/\, r^3{}_{ij}\,(t) \Big]$$

and $J'\, (\nu)$ is the intensity of

$$\sum_j {}^1/_2 \sqrt{3}\, m_j\,(t)\,\sin\vartheta_{ij}\,(t)\,\cos\vartheta_{ij}\,(t)\,e^{i\,\varphi_{ij}\,(t)}\,/r^3_{ij}\,(t)$$

These intensities represent the spectrum of the local magnetic field.

Identical expressions exist for transitions with $\triangle m_i = -1$. In that case the intensities have to be taken at positive frequencies in the Fourier spectrum. We shall see later that $J\,(\nu)$ is an even function. This is plausible, since the negative frequencies have no specific physical meaning and are merely a consequence of complex notation. One might object that on this basis the thermal motion would produce as many transitions upward as downward, and still the desired energy dissipation would not occur. Since we have to do, however, with a thermal mechanism, it is appropriate to weight the transition probabilities with the Bolzmann factor of the final state. Dealing with the interaction with radiation, E i n s t e i n did essentially the same thing by introducing the spontaneous emission, so as to increase the number of downward transitions. This procedure can be justified by postulating that in the case of equilibrium we have a Bolzmann distribution over the energy levels and a detailed balance for each transition process (G 6).

$$N_q\,W_{p\leftarrow q} = N_p\,W_{q\leftarrow p}$$

$$N_q/N_p = \exp\,(E_p - E_q)/k\,T \qquad (2.43)$$

$$W_{p\leftarrow q}/W_{q\leftarrow p} = \exp\,(E_q - E_p)/k\,T$$

In the case that $I = {}^1/_2$ we can write down the differential equation for the population in the upper and lower state in the same way as we did in dealing with the interaction with radiation (section 2. 3)

$$\frac{d\,N^+}{d\,T} = W\,N^+ exp\,\frac{\gamma\,\hbar\,H_0}{2\,k\,T} + W\,N^-\,exp - \frac{\gamma\,\hbar\,H_0}{2\,k\,T}$$

$$N^+ + N^- = N \qquad (2.44)$$

$$W \approx (W_{\triangle m = +1} + W_{\triangle m = -1})/2$$

Expanding the exponentials and keeping only terms of the first order in $\gamma\,\hbar\,H_0/k\,T$, the solution becomes

$$N^{+\cdot} = C\,e^{-2\,W\,t} + {}^1/_2\,N\,(1 - \gamma\,\hbar\,H_0/2\,k\,T) \qquad (2.45)$$

The constant C is determined by the initial conditions at $t = 0$. So

N^+ approaches its equilibrium value asymptotically according to an exponential function with a characteristic time given by

$$T_1 = 1/2 \ W \tag{2.46}$$

The surplus number $n = N - 2 N^+$ has the same characteristic relaxation time. For W we shall take the value given by the formulæ (2.40) to (2.42), although this is not quite correct for the processes with $\triangle m = \pm 2$, nor for the case, that there are different magnetogyric ratios.

Then we should solve a more complicated system of simultaneous differential equations.

The case that $I > {}^1/_2$ is more complicated. If there are only two possible orientations of the spin, a temperature of the spin system can always be defined by the relation $N^+/N^- = \exp(- \gamma \hbar H_0/k \ T)$.

If $I > {}^1/_2$, a temperature can only be defined if

$$N_I/N_{I-1} = N_{I-1}/N_{I-2} = \ldots \qquad = \exp(- \gamma \hbar H_0/k \ T) \tag{2.47}$$

We require that this condition is fulfilled at $t = 0$. It is easily checked for the case $I = 1$ by solving a set of three simultaneous differential equations for N_1, N_0, N_{-1} that the relation (2.47) is in general not satisfied at all times. We shall prove, however, that for $\delta = \gamma \hbar H_0/k \ T \ll 1$, a temperature and a relaxation time can always be defined. There is hardly a loss of generality, since the condition $\delta \ll 1$ is fulfilled down to 0.1 °K. We start from the set of $2 I + 1$ equations

$$\frac{d N_I}{d t} = - W_{I-1, I} N_I + W_{I, I-1} N_{I-1} \tag{2.48}$$

$$\frac{d N_{I-1}}{d t} = (- W_{I-2, I-1} - W_{I, I-1}) N_{I-1} + W_{I-1, I} N_I + W_{I-1, I-2} N_{I-2}$$

etc. with

$$W_{m+1, m} = W (I - m)(I + m + 1) \exp(- m \ \delta), \tag{2.49}$$

where W is the transition probability from the state $m = {}^1/_2$ to $m = {}^1/_2$, if $I = {}^1/_2$.

From (2.49) we derive a set of linear combinations for $N_m + N_{-m}$

$$\frac{d (N_m + N_{-m})}{d t} = - W_{m+1, m} + W_{m-1, m}) (N_m + N_{-m}) +$$
$$+ W_{m, m+m} (N_{m+1} + N_{-m-1}) + W_{m, m-1}(N_{m-1} + N_{-m+1}) +$$
$$+ 2 m \ \delta N_{-m} + 2 (m + 1) \ \delta N_{-m-1} + 2 (m - 1) \ \delta N_{-m+1} \tag{2.50}$$

The last three terms on the right hand side can be neglected compared to the first three.

Next we derive a set of equations for $N_m - N_{-m}$. We make use of the relation $2 m \delta N_{-m} = N_m^\infty - N_{-m}^\infty$, the difference of the population of the levels m and $-m$ at thermal equilibrium. We obtain

$$\frac{d(N_m - N_{-m})}{dt} = -(W_{m+1,m} + W_{m-1,m})[N_m - N_m^\infty - (N_{-m} - N_{-m}^\infty)] +$$

$$+ W_{m,m+1}[N_{m+1} - N_{m+1}^\infty - (N_{-m-1} - N_{-m-1}^\infty)] +$$

$$+ W_{m,m-1}[(N_{m-1} - N_{m-1}^\infty) - (N_{-m+1} - N_{-m+1}^\infty)] \quad (2.51)$$

Equations (2. 50) can be solved by anticipating that $N_m + N_{-m}$ is independent of the time, $N_m + N_{-m} = 2 N/2 I + 1$. If I is an integer, $N_0 = N/2 I + 1$ is constant in time. The solution of the equations (2. 51) is obtained by making the supposition that the difference in population between two adjacent levels $n = N_m - N_{-m}/2 m$ is independent of m. We find that the set (2. 51) reduces to a single equation

$$\frac{dn}{dt} = -2 W (n - n^\infty) \quad (2.52)$$

The result is that the relaxation time for a nucleus with spin I is the same as for a nucleus with the same magnetogyric ratio, but spin $1/2$. Using (2. 40) we find for the relaxation time

$$1/T_1 = {}^3/_4 \gamma^4 \hbar^2 I (I+1) [J_2 (2\nu_0) + 2J_1 (\nu_0)] \quad (2.53)$$

and analogous expressions besides the equations (2. 41) and (2. 42).

2. 6. The line width.

We now return to the terms A and B in (2. 34) to see what happens to the line width, when the nuclei are changing their positions as they take part in the Brownian motion. These terms will still represent secular perturbations, if we take the components near zero frequency in $J_0 (\nu)$, the Fourier spectrum of $\Sigma_j (1 - 3 \cos^2 \vartheta_{ij} (t)) / r_{ij}^3 (t)$. The question is, which frequencies must be considered to be „near zero". We may say that the perturbation is secular up to that frequency, for which $h \nu$ is of the same order as the actual splitting of the energy levels by the perturbation. The actual width expressed in cycles /sec may be called

$2 \triangle \nu = \triangle \omega / \pi = 1 / \pi T_2'$. A combination of (2. 36) and (2. 37) yields the relation for the width

$$\frac{1}{T_2'} = {}^3/_2 \, \gamma^2 \, \hbar \sqrt{\frac{I(I+1)}{3}} \int_{-1/\pi T_2'}^{+1/\pi T_2'} J_0(\nu) \, d\nu \qquad (2.54)$$

If the nuclei do not all have the same magnetogyric ratio, we can alter the treatment for term A in the same way as we did in the preceding section for T_1. The term B, however, changes its character completely, because it now contains a time factor $\exp i (\gamma_1 - \gamma_2) H_0 \, t$. The components of $J_0(\nu)$ at $\nu = \pm (\gamma_1 - \gamma_2) H_0 / 2 \pi$ determine the transition probability for a process in which to antiparallel nuclei with different magnetogyric ratios jump together. We shall not discuss it further.

The observed line width is not determined by T_2' only. There also is a contribution arising from the finite life time of the nucleus in a given state by the relaxation processes, represented by the terms C, D, E and F. For $I = {}^1/_2$, the life time of both the upper and lower level is $1/W = 2T_1$. As Weisskopf and Wigner (W 3) pointed out, we have to think that each of these levels is broadened into a continuous distribution .

$$g^1(\nu) \, d\nu = \frac{W}{4 \pi^2 (\nu - \nu_0)^2 + {}^1/_4 \, W^2} \, d\nu$$

The distribution in the intensity of a resonance transition between the two levels is consequently

$$g(\nu) = \frac{2 T_1 (\nu_0^2 + \nu^2)}{\nu^2 + 4 \pi^2 (\nu_0^2 - \nu^2)^2 \, T_1^2}$$

or to a high degree of approximation

$$g(\nu) \approx \frac{4 T_1}{1 + 16 \pi^2 T_1^2 (\nu - \nu_0)^2} \qquad (2.55)$$

This is the broadening caused by the finite relaxation time T_1. The distribution over the resonance frequencies, caused by the perturbation A and B, will often have an approximately Gaussian shape,

$$g^{11}(\nu) = T_2' \sqrt{\frac{1}{2\pi}} \, e^{-2 \pi^2 (\nu - \nu_0)^2 \, T_2'^2} \qquad (2.56)$$

Combining (2. 55) and (2. 56) we get for the line shape

$$\varphi(\nu) = \sqrt{\frac{8}{\pi}} \, T_1 \, T_2' \int_{-\infty}^{+\infty} \frac{e^{-2 \pi^2 (\nu^1 - \nu_0)^2 \, T_2'^2}}{1 + 16 \pi^2 (\nu^1 - \nu)^2 \, T_1^2} \, d\nu^1 \qquad (2.57)$$

Roughly we can say that the combination of two bell shaped curves will yield another bell shaped curve, of which the width is about the sum of the widths of the composing curves. We can express the total line width by

$$\frac{1}{T_2} \approx \frac{1}{T_2'} + \frac{1}{2\,T_1} \qquad (2.58)$$

Instead of the unwieldy distribution (2.57), we shall assume that $\varphi(v)$ can be well represented either by a Gaussian distribution like (2.56) or by a damped oscillator distribution like (2.55). This may seem

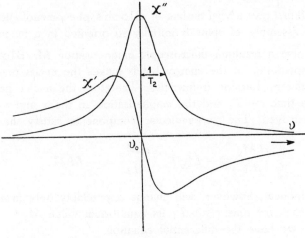

Figure 2.4.

The behaviour of the real and imaginary part of the magnetic susceptibility near resonance. The curves are drawn for the case of a damped harmonic oscillator (compare section 2.7).

arbitrary, but the choice of (2.56) was already arbitrary, and the two possibilities, which we admit, are good representatives for the case that there are practically no tails (gaussian), and that the tails of the resonance curve contribute considerably (damped oscillator). Note that in the latter case $2/T_2$ is the total width between the half maximum points. For the Gaussian $1/T_2$ denotes the root mean square deviation of the frequency. This quantity diverges for the damped oscillator curve.

We have derived general expressions for the relaxation time and line width in terms of the local field spectrum. In order to evaluate these quantities for any given substance, we only have to compute the in-

❦❦

tensity of this spectrum. In chapter 4 applications are given for solids, liquids and gases.

The meaning of the quantities T_1 and T_2' in terms of the density function $f(v)$ represented in fig. 2.3 might be formulated in the following manner. The time, which is required to restore the shape of $f(v)$ around the frequency v_0 after the equilibrium has been disturbed in some way or other, is T_2'. The time required to restore the area under the $f(v)$ curve around v_0 is T_1. We shall now see how the introduction of the quantities T_1 and T_2, which describe the interactions between the spins, changes the results obtained in the beginning of this chapter for free spins.

2.7. Classical theory with interactions.

We shall first give a brief outline of Bloch's phenomenological theory (B 4). An assembly of spins is initially so oriented in a magnetic field $\vec{H_0}$ as to give a resultant macroscopic magnetisation $\vec{M}$. Bloch notes that the spreading of the energy levels makes the nuclei precess with slightly different Larmor frequencies. Therefore the nuclei get out of phase in a time $t \sim T_2$ and the magnetisation in the x and y-direction will be destroyed. The perpendicular components satisfy the equation

$$\frac{dM_x}{dt} = -M_x/T_2 \qquad \frac{dM_y}{dt} = -M_y/T_2 \qquad (2.59)$$

The z-component, however, will change appreciably only in a time T_1, and will reach for time $t \gg T_1$ its equilibrium value M_0.

For M_z we have the differential equation

$$\frac{dM_z}{dt} = -(M_z - M_0)/T_1 \qquad (2.60)$$

Bloch mentions that $T_1 \gg T_2$. We shall see in chapter 4 that this is not always the case, and in the following no use of this inequality is made. We can now write down the equations of motion in case of an applied r.f. field by modifying the equations (2.59) and (2.60) to

$$\frac{dM_z}{dt} = \gamma [\vec{H} \times \vec{M}]_z + (M_0 - M_z)/T_1$$

$$\frac{dM_{x,y}}{dt} = \gamma [\vec{H} \times \vec{M}]_{x,y} - M_{x,y}/T_2$$

$$(2.61)$$

To solve these equations, for a magnetic field (1.10)

✣✣

$$H_x = H_1 \cos \omega t, \; H_y = H_1 \sin \omega t \text{ and } H_z = H_0$$

transform again to a rotating coordinate system

$$M_x = u \cos \omega t - v \sin \omega t$$

$$M_y = \pm (u \sin \omega t + v \cos \omega t)$$

The — sign is used for negative γ. Using the abbreviations

$$\tau = b t$$

$$b = |\gamma| H_1$$

$$a = 1/b T_1$$

$$\beta = 1/b T_2$$

$$\delta = (\omega_0 - \omega)/b = \triangle \omega/b$$

the equations of motion reduce to

$$\frac{d u}{d \tau} + \beta u + \delta v = 0$$

$$\frac{d v}{d \tau} + \beta v - \delta u + M_z = 0 \qquad (2.62)$$

$$\frac{d M_z}{d \tau} + a M_z - v = a$$

A time independent solution is possible with $\dfrac{d u}{d \tau} = \dfrac{d v}{d \tau} = \dfrac{d M_z}{d \tau} = 0$,

we obtain: $M_z = \dfrac{1 + (T_2 \triangle \omega)^2}{1 + (T_2 \triangle \omega)^2 + (\gamma H_1)^2 T_1 T_2} M_0$

$$u = \frac{|\gamma| H_1 T_2 (\triangle \omega T_2)}{1 + (T_2 \triangle \omega)^2 + (\gamma H_1)^2 T_1 T_2} M_0$$

$$\qquad (2.63)$$

$$v = \frac{-|\gamma| H_1 T_2}{1 + (T_2 \triangle \omega)^2 + (\gamma H_1)^2 T_1 T_2} M_0$$

The strength of the resonance effect we want to measure is — as will be shown in more detail in the next chapter — proportional to the components of the magnetisation perpendicular to H_0, which vary with the same frequency as the applied signal. We shall therefore maximize

~~~~~~

46

the expressions (2. 63) for u and v with respect to the frequency ω and the applied field H_1.

We see immediately that the out-of-phase component v of the magnetisation which is responsible for absorption, is maximal for $\triangle \omega = 0$. The optimal value

$$v = {}^1\!/_2 \ M_0 \ \sqrt{T_2/T_1} \tag{2.64}$$

is then obtained if $\gamma^2 H_1^2 T_1 T_2 = 1$.

The component u, which is in phase with the magnetic field H_1 and describes the dispersion, reaches asymptotically the same maximum value as v for $\triangle \omega = \sqrt{1 + \gamma^2 H_1^2 T_1 T_2}/T_1$ and $\gamma^2 H_1^2 T_1 T_2 \gg 1$.

If we introduce the complex magnetic susceptibility $\chi = \chi' - i \chi''$ and write $\vec{M} = \chi \vec{H}$, then it follows that $u = \chi' H_1$, $v = \chi'' H_1$ and from (2.63)

$$\chi' = \frac{|\gamma| \ T_2 \ (\triangle \omega \ T_2) \ \chi_0 \ H_0}{1 + (T_2 \ \triangle \omega)^2 + \gamma^2 H_1^2 T_1 T_2} \tag{2.65}$$

$$\chi'' = \frac{|\gamma| \ T_2 \ \chi_0 \ H_0}{1 + (T_2 \ \triangle \omega)^2 + \gamma^2 H_1^2 T_1 T_2} \tag{2.66}$$

where $\chi_0 = M_0/H_0$ is the static susceptibility (1. 18).

The susceptibility must be considered to have different values for the three components of $\vec{H}$. For the z-component of H and the component rotating in the opposite direction around the z-axis, the susceptibility has the static value χ_0; no resonance phenomenon occurs. We see from (2. 63), (2. 65) that in strong radio-frequency fields of the resonating component a saturation effect occurs. The susceptibilities decrease for $\gamma^2 H_1^2 T_1 T_2 \gg 1$ in proportion to H_1^{-2}. The externally induced transitions then compete too succesfully with the transitions caused by the relaxation mechanism. In the case $T_1 = \infty$, the magnetisation is zero. This is the heating up (1. 24) in a system of free spins. In the limit $H_1 \to 0$, when $\gamma^2 H_1^2 T_1 T_2 \ll 1$, the line shape (2. 65) is identical with a damped oscillator curve like (2. 55), as shown in fig. 2. 4. This is no surprise, since we have rather arbitrarily assumed the exponential decay of the perpendicular components in (2. 59). The reasoning in this section cannot be considered as a proof that the line shape near resonance is the same as that of a damped harmonic oscillator. In the preceding sections we have already seen that this is in general not the case. Bloch's classical equations (2. 62) are especially useful to obtain solutions for non-stationary phenomena and transient effects (B 7). For these the reader is referred to the original literature.

2.8. *Quantumtheory with interactions.*

We shall now derive the saturation formulæ for absorption and dispersion in the stationary state along quantummechanical lines (G 6, K 8). We start with the absorption for $I = \frac{1}{2}$. The situation to be described is that of a competition between the applied signal and the local field spectrum, the former tending to make the surplus number $n = N^+ - N^-$ zero, the latter to keep it at the value of temperature equilibrium

$$n_0 = \frac{N^+ + N^-}{2} \; \gamma \, \frac{\hbar H_0}{kT}.$$

The surplus number n can formally be thought of as being distributed over a frequency range according to a function $\varphi(\nu)$, as was discussed in section 2.6.

$$n(\nu) = n \, \varphi(\nu) \qquad \int_0^\infty \varphi(\nu) \, d\nu = 1 \tag{2.67}$$

The frequency of the applied signal $H_1 = \int H_1(\nu) \, d\nu$ is so well defined, that $\varphi(\nu)$ can be considered as constant over the region where H_1 is different from zero. In the radio frequency range such a pure sine wave for H_1 is practically realisable. According to (2.16) this signal causes a surplus number of transitions per second

$$\tfrac{1}{4} \gamma^2 H_1^2 \, n \, \varphi(\nu) \tag{2.68}$$

In the stationary state this must be equal and opposite to the number of transitions caused by the relaxation mechanism.

$$-W(n - n_0) = -(n - n_0)/2 T_1 \tag{2.69}$$

Equating expressions (2.68) and (2.69), we find for n in the stationary state

$$n = n_0 \frac{1}{1 + \frac{1}{2} T_1 H_1^2 \gamma^2 \varphi(\nu)} \tag{2.70}$$

The power absorbed in the stationary state is obtained by substituting (2.70) in the expression (2.68) and multiplying by the energy $h\nu = \gamma \hbar H_0$ absorbed in each transition. Here we assume that the shape of the distribution of the surplus number is independent of H_1.

$$P = \frac{\frac{1}{4} n_0 \, \varphi(\nu) \, \gamma^2 H_1^2 \, \gamma \hbar H_0}{1 + \frac{1}{2} \gamma^2 H_1^2 T_1 \, \varphi(\nu)} \tag{2.71}$$

✢✢✢

48

The absorbed power can be expressed in terms of the complex susceptibility. The energy of the system is

$$-\int \vec{M} \cdot d\vec{H} = -\int \vec{M} \cdot \frac{d\vec{H}}{dt} dt.$$

The power absorbed by it,

$$P = \frac{-d}{dt} \int \vec{M} \cdot \frac{d\vec{H}}{dt} dt = -\vec{M} \cdot \dot{\vec{H}},$$

is made up from the contributions of v in the x- and y-component of M. With the use of $v = \chi'' H_1$ the result for the average absorbed power is

$$P = \omega \chi'' H_1^2 \qquad (2.73)$$

From (2.71) and (2.73) we find

$$\chi'' = \frac{1}{4} n_0 \gamma^2 \hbar \frac{\varphi(\nu)}{1 + \frac{1}{2} \gamma^2 H_1^2 T_1 \varphi(\nu)} \qquad (2.74)$$

Using the relation $M = \frac{1}{2} n_0 \gamma \hbar$, $\omega \approx \gamma H_0$ near resonance, and taking for $\varphi(\nu)$ a distribution (2.55) we get back to Bloch's expression (2.66), as it should be.

If $I \neq \frac{1}{2}$, we must have a detailed balance for transitions between each pair of adjacent levels. The transitions probabilities for the applied signal and the relaxation mechanism depend in the same way on m_I. With the result of (2.52) the difference in population between any two adjacent levels is again given by (2.70), where now $n_0 = \frac{N}{2I+1} \frac{\gamma \hbar H_0}{kT}$.

Already in (1.16) we have seen that the result of summing over all values of m leads to the result, that the power absorbed is proportional to $I(I+1)$. So we find immediately

$$\chi'' = \frac{1}{3} N H_0 \frac{\gamma^3 \hbar^2}{kT} \frac{\varphi(\nu)}{1 + \frac{1}{2} \gamma^2 H_1^2 T_1 \varphi(\nu)} I(I+1) \qquad (2.75)$$

The spin I can be determined from the total line intensity.

The corresponding formulæ for the dispersion can be derived by a general theorem. Kramers (K 7, K 9) showed that the relation

$$\chi'(\nu) = \frac{2}{\pi} \int_0^\infty \frac{\nu' \chi''(\nu')}{\nu'^2 - \nu^2} d\nu' \qquad (2.76)$$

exists between the real and imaginary part of an electric or magnetic susceptibility. But if the absorption (2.74) is described by Bloch's expression (2.65) for χ'' also the corresponding dispersion must be described by the expression (2.66) for χ'. The integration (2.76) must give this result (2.66).

We have not emphasized a very important assumption in the derivation of the saturation formulæ. The distribution function $\varphi(\nu)$ has been taken independent of H_1, that is: the shape of the distribution of the surplus nuclei is independent of the saturation. In fig. 2.5. the ori-

Figure 2. 5.

The distribution of the surplus population over the resonance frequencies.
a) No saturation
b) Saturation without change of shape
c) Partial saturation in inhomogeneous fields.

ginal distribution is represented by curve a, b is a saturated distribution of the same shape, and will be realised, if $T_1 \gg 1/\gamma H_1 \gg T_2$. Then the rapid spin-spin interaction will be able to maintain the distribution b, although the signal only induces transitions near the frequency ν. The assumption is still approximately true if $T_1 \gg 1/\gamma H_1$ and $T_2 \gg 1/\gamma H_1$. For then the large applied field will produce transitions over the whole width of the resonance curve. But in this case formula (2.65) is not quite correct as follows from the consideration, that in the limit of very large H_1, we must get Rabi's formula (2.11) with a line width $\triangle \omega = \gamma H_1$, while (2.65) gives

$$\triangle \omega = \gamma H_1 \sqrt{T_1/T_2}$$

One might infer from this that the saturation is still rather well des-

++

cribed by (2.71), if T_1 is of the same order as T_2. In chapter 4 we shall see that this is the case for liquids ands gases. For a special model of He-gas the Bloch formula will be derived in a independent way. The assumption that the shape of the distribution function does not change is definitely wrong, if the distribution is mainly determined by inhomogeneities $\triangle H$ in the field H_0. In this case the saturated distribution will look like curve c in fig. 2.5. The nuclei which are in another part of the field are not at resonance and there the unsaturated distribution $h(\nu)$ remains. The line shape, determined by a point-by-point measurement at various frequencies ν of the applied signal, is always $h(\nu)$, independent of the degree of saturation. We have in general:

$$\chi'' = \gamma M_0 \int_{-0}^{+\infty} \frac{T_2}{1 + T_2^2 (\omega - \omega')^2 + \gamma^2 H_1^2 T_1 T_2} \, h(\nu') d\nu' \quad (2.77)$$

If $h(\nu)$ varies only slowly in the region where transitions are appreciable this becomes

$$\chi'' = h(\nu) \gamma M_0 \int_{-\infty}^{+\infty} \frac{T_2}{1 + (T_2 \triangle \omega')^2 + \gamma^2 H_1^2 T_1 T_2} \, d\nu'$$

$$= h(\nu) \frac{\gamma M_0}{2 \sqrt{1 + \gamma^2 H_1^2 T_1 T_2}} \quad (2.78)$$

Finally it must be stressed that all formulæ are derived for a rotating magnetic field. Experimentally always an oscillating field is used. This, however, can be decomposed into two fields rotating in opposite directions. The field $H_x = 2 H_1 \cos \omega t$. $H_y = 0$ is equivalent to the set

$$H_x = H_1 \cos \omega t \qquad H_x = H_1 \cos \omega t$$
$$H_y = H_1 \sin \omega t \qquad H_y = - H_1 \sin \omega t \qquad (2.79)$$

Now only one of these — the right or left circular polarised one for a positive or negative magnetogyric ratio respectively — will be effective in producing transitions. The transition probability, the absorbed power, the components of magnetisation u and v etc. in a linear oscillating field with amplitude $2 H_1$ are the same as in the rotating field with a component H_1 perpendicular to H_0, for which all discussions were made. If one prefers to express the magnetisation u and v in terms of the linear field H_1, one must use a susceptibility χ_{lin}, which is one half of that occuring in (2.65). Note that $H_1{}^2$ in the saturation term of that formula must be replaced by $^1/_4 H_1{}^2$. The maximum value of the magnetisation χH_1 remains unchanged:

$$u_{max} = v_{max} = {}^1/_2 M_0 \sqrt{T_2/T_1}$$

The reader can easily adapt the other formulæ to the case of a linear field H_1. Bloch and Siegert (B 9) have discussed the influence of the other rotating component, which we neglected. The resonance frequency is displaced by $(H_1/H_0)^2 \nu_0$ in order of magnitude. Under experimental conditions one always has $H_1/H_0 < 10^{-3}$. So this correction is completely negligible. The only disadvantage of a linear field is that the sign of the magnetogyric ratio cannot be determined. Nevertheless this information has been obtained from resonance experiments, for which we must refer to the literature (M 3).

CHAPTER III.

THE EXPERIMENTAL METHOD.

3. 1. *The experimental arrangement.*

3. 1. 1. *The original experiment, by Purcell, Torrey and Pound.*

From the preceding chapters it should be clear that the problem is to measure a small change of the magnetic susceptibility in the radio-frequency range, caused by the resonance of the nuclei. The essential part of the apparatus will therefore be a coil, placed in a constant magnetic field H_0 and filled with a material, which contains the nuclei to be investigated. The coil is tuned by a condenser in parallel, and a current in the coil is excited by coupling it to a generator. The position of the coil is such, that the radio-frequency field in the coil is perpendicular to H_0. On the other hand the circuit is coupled to the input of a receiver, tuned to the same frequency. At the output of the receiver we measure the transmission through the LC-circuit. We vary H_0 slowly. On hitting the resonance of the nuclei at the value $H_0 = 2 \pi \nu_0/\gamma$, a change in the output reading will be recorded, as the absorption by the nuclei lowers the Q of the LC-circuit by a small amount. The quality factor Q is defined by

$$Q = 2 \pi \frac{\text{energy stored in the circuit}}{\text{power dissipated per cycle}} \qquad (3. 1).$$

At resonance the power absorbed per unit time is increased by the energy absorption of the system of nuclei. The real part of the nuclear susceptibility causes a shift in phase of the radio-frequency signal, which was not detected by the original arrangement. It is plausible, and will be proved in section 2 of this chapter, that the relative decrease in voltage across the coil is proportional to the change in the nuclear susceptibility and the Q of the coil. In the original experiment by Purcell, Torrey and Pound, the resonant circuit consisted of a short length of coaxial line, tuned by a capacitance to 30 Mc/sec as shown in fig. 3. 1. The power was inductively coupled in and out by

⚡⚡

small loops A and B. The inductive part of the cavity was filled with 850 cc. paraffin. The Q obtained was 670. Assuming a line width of 5 oersted in paraffin, a change in χ of the order of 3.10^{-6} could be expected, corresponding to a change of less than 1 % in output power.

To increase the relative change a bridge circuit was built, which balanced out the main part of the signal going into the receiver. By means of an attenuator and pieces of coaxial line of variable length the signal going through one branch could be adjusted so as to have about the same amplitude and 180° phase shift with respect to the signal going through the cavity in the other branch of the bridge.

▨ Brass
▨ Copper
▨ Mica

s cm

Figure 3. 1.

Cavity, used in the first experiment of nuclear magnetic resonance. The cavity was filled with 850 cc. Paraffin.

At the resonance of the protons in the paraffin the output changed by 50 %. The change was positive or negative depending on the way the bridge was balanced. The resonance occurred at that value of the magnetic field H_0, which could be expected from Rabi's measurement of the proton moment and the resonance frequency used. With the same circuit also the resonance of H^1 and F^{19} nuclei were observed in a mixture of Ca F_2 powder and mineral oil. The amplitude of the radio-frequency field in the cavity was kept as low as possible ($< 10^{-4}$ oersted) in order to avoid saturation. From (2. 65) we see that saturation occurs if $\gamma^2 H_1^2 T_1 T_2 \approx 1$.

Assuming $T_2 = 10^{-5}$ sec, corresponding to a width of the proton line of about 3 oersted, we find that the relaxation time could be about four hours without saturating the spin system. An upper limit for the relaxation time in paraffin of 60 sec was established by observing the resonance as quickly as possible after the magnetic field H_0 is applied. Immediately after the field is switched on, the relative population of the protons in the upper and lower level will be given by the a-priori probabilities of these levels, which are equal. Therefore a resonance can only be observed after a time comparable to the relaxation time has elapsed. This upper limit of 60 sec is historically important, since the available information at that time, consisting of Waller's theory and Gorter's experiments, indicated very long relaxation times.

3. 1. 2. *Further experimental development.*

Already in their first papers Purcell, Torrey and Pound (P 3) mentioned the advantage of modulating the magnetic field H_0 with an alternating field of small amplitude and low frequency,

$$H_z = H_0 + H_s \sin \omega_s t \qquad (3.2)$$

The method of modulation had been applied in other fields on many occasions (e.g. in photo-electric amplifiers (M2)). The advantage is not an improvement in the essential signal-to-noise ratio, but a reduction of the influence of external disturbances. Instead of measuring the d-c output of the detector directly, in the modulation method the audio-frequency signal is fed, after detection, into an audio-amplifier which has a very narrow band around the frequency ω_s, which was taken equal to half the frequency of the mains, i.e. 30 cycles per second. One could use an ordinary audio-amplifier with an a.c. galvanometer at the output. Actually a phase-sensitive „lock-in" amplifier (D3) was used, which will be described in the next section. The cavity was replaced by a coil, of about 2 cm long and 0.7 cm in diameter, tuned by a variable condensor. The quality factor was about 10 times smaller for this circuit compared to the preceding one, corresponding to a similar decrease in linear dimensions. This implies, of course, a loss in signal strength. The cavity, however, required a large magnet, which was not permanently available. Furthermore even in the large magnet the field was not homogeneous over the region of the cavity, so that the maximum signal from the nuclei was decreased according to the lower value of h (ν) in (2.78). In addition the cavity required unwieldy and sometimes not available quantities of material. Also the bridge circuit was improved as described in the next section.

Figure 3. 2.
Block diagram of the experimental arrangement, which is described in sections 3.1.3. and 3.1.4.

With the apparatus represented schematically in fig. 3. 2 the nuclear resonance could be observed either on the screen of the oscilloscope or on the output L of the 30 ~ audio amplifier. In the first case the amplitude of the 30 ~ modulation sweep is larger than the line width. On passing through the line the detector current measured by M changes proportional to the absorption by the nuclei, if the bridge is balanced properly. The change in voltage across a resistor in the detector circuit is put directly on the vertically deflecting plates of the cathode ray tube. On the horizontal plates we put a synchronous 30 ~ sine sweep. On the screen appear two absorption curves, because in each cycle the sweep passes twice through resonance. The two curves can be made to coincide by proper adjustment of the phase of the horizontal sweep (see fig 3. 15). By changing the main field H_0 the absorption lines would shift together and finally disappear from the screen. A section of the magnetic field from $H_0 - H_s$ to $H_0 + H_s$ is plotted in the horizontal direction on the oscilloscope. For observation on the meter L the sweep amplitude was made small compared to the line width. As will be shown later the deflection of this meter was then at any point H_0 proportional to the derivative of the curve on the oscilloscope at the corresponding field strength. By changing H_0 very slowly the entire derivative function could be measured point by point. We shall now describe the apparatus in the block diagram in more detail.

3. 1. 3. *The radiofrequency bridge.*

It is important to be able to balance the bridge independently in amplitude and phase. To obtain these two orthogonal adjustments first the circuit shown in fig. 3. 3. was used. The various parts are linked together with coaxial lines, of which the outer conductors are

Figure 3. 3.

Radio-frequency bridge, described in the text.
$C_1 = 3 \, \mu\mu F$ $C_2 = 5 \, \mu\mu F$ $C = 100 \, \mu\mu F$.

connected to the grounded terminals of the generator, resonant circuit and receiver. The attenuator A was of the inductive type, used for 10 cm. waves. The inner conductors of the coaxial lines were terminated in small loops, the distance between which could be varied. The attenuation between the loops is characteristic for a wave guide (K 11) „beyond cut-off". At 30 Mc/sec the impedance of the loops is practically zero. The attenuation is large and not accompanied by a noticeable phase shift. In order to obtain the same low transmission in the other branch a very short closed stub S was inserted, which also acted practically like a short circuit. To this voltage generator of very low internal impedance the resonance circuit was loosely coupled by a small condenser C_1, while on the other side it was critically coupled to the receiver input by another condenser C_2. The non-resonant line between P and the carbon resistor R, which is equal to the characteristic impedance of the coaxial cable is of variable length and provides a pure phase adjustment. The lines of one quarter wave length transform the short circuits into open circuits. Looking from the generator into the bridge one „sees" the resistance R. This expression means that the impedance between the two terminals of the bridge at the side of the generator is R. Between the terminals, which are connected to the input of the receiver, is the impedance of the LC circuit, tranformed by C_2. If this coupling has the desired critical value, the maximum available power from the resonance circuit will flow into the receiver. The disadvantages of this bridge are its low transmission and its asymmetry. The minimum attenuation is about 40 db, and the generator has to be unnecessarily powerful. The power required for the nuclear experiments is essentially low, but since the maximum output of the available generator was 2V. into 75 Ω, it was desirable not to waste too much power.

The asymmetry of the bridge allowed a balance of the bridge only at one frequency. Since the generator showed some frequency modulation, this was very undesirable. Moreover was the balance sensitive to very slow drifts of the frequency. Therefore the circuit of fig. 3. 4 was adopted for the final measurements. The generator power is fed into two coaxial lines of equal length terminated in their characteristic impedance. The condensers C_1 and C_2 provide a loose coupling to the resonance circuits, which are tuned at exactly the same frequency and have the same Q. The output condensers C_3 and C_4 provide critical coupling between the resonance circuits and the receiver, for which the two circuits appear in parallel.

Since part of the change in power from the nuclear resonance now flows into the dummy circuit instead of into the receiver, the available signal-to-noise power ratio is only one half of the optimal value, obtained

✧✧

57

Figure 3. 4.

Improved radio-frequency bridge, described in the text.
$R_1 = R_2 = 50 \, \Omega$
$C_1 = 3 \, \mu\mu \, F$, $C_2 = C_7 = C_8 = 5 \, \mu\mu \, F$, $C_3 = C_4 = 4 \, \mu\mu \, F$
$C_5 = C_6 = 60 \, \mu\mu \, F$.

with the preceding diagram. A coaxial line of one half wave length produces a phase shift of 180° degrees. For reasons to be discussed in the next section, the balance was never made complete. When the remaining unbalance is in amplitude, the imaginary part of the nuclear susceptibility is measured; when the remainder is phase unbalance, the phase shift of the signal and thus the real part is measured. The unbalance used in the experiments varied from 0.1 to 0.001 in amplitude of the original signal (20-60 db) and was stable at these values. For short time intervals balance to one part in 30000 (90 db) could be obtained. The ratio by which the signal is reduced in the bridge we shall call *b*. The radiofrequency coil, which is placed in the magnetic field, is shown in fig. 3. 8. The coil consists in a typical example of 11 turns of copper wire of 0.1 cm diameter. The length of the coil is 1.7 cm, and its inside diameter 0.6 cm. Samples, contained in thin walled cylindrical glass vessels of approximately 0.5 cc, could easily be placed in the coil and replaced. The brass box, which was below the magnet gap, contained the other circuit elements of the nuclear resonance circuit in fig. 3. 4.

With the trimmer C_7 minor adjustments in the phase could be made. The dummy circuit contained essentially the same elements, although no particular care was taken to make a geometrical copy. For the dummy the resonance frequency was adjusted by selecting the tuning capacitance C_6; the coupling condenser C_2 formed together with C_8 a differential air trimmer. If C_2 increased, C_8 decreased by about the same amount and this provided a phase-independent adjustment of the amplitude for the balance of the bridge. The Q of the dummy was made equal to that of the nuclear resonance circuit by putting a carbon resistor R_3 as a parallel load on the circuit. The analysis and trimming was done by connecting the resonance circuits to a signal generator and measuring the transmission as a function of the frequency with a sylvania crystal detector, shown in fig. 3.5. Resonance circuits were also made for 14.4 Mc/sec and 4.85 Mc/sec respectively. As a matter of fact, the same size of coil was used and only the condensers were adjusted. Of course also the half wave length cable had to be changed, which at the lowest frequency had a length of about twenty meters. The Amphenol cables have a polythene dielectric and a characteristic impedance of 50 Ω. It might be worth while to obtain the 180° phase shift by a radio frequency transformer with centre-grounded secondary instead of a difference in line length, although the method used by us proved to be successful.

Figure 3. 5.

Crystal detector with galvanometer.

3. 1. 4. *Other apparatus.*

The signal generator was of the type General Radio 805 C. The frequency ranged from 16 kc to 50 Mc. The output could be varied continuously from 0.1 μ V to 2 V. The characteristic output impedance was 75 Ω. So there was a mismatch of three to one with the bridge. This was harmless and no attempt was made to eliminate it, as could be done, e.g. by a quarter wave transformer, The receiver is a National H R O 5. The narrow passband of this instrument (1500 cycles/second) was of little use in the present experiment. It necessitated more frequent adjustments of the tuning. Only for observation with the oscilloscope it improved the signal to noise ratio. The H R O 5 was fed by an electronically regulated power supply. In the experiments at 30 Mc/sec the receiver was preceded by a pre- amplifier, developed at the Radiation Laboratory, Cambridge (Mass.). Originally designed for use in Radar equipment, it had a pass band from 25-35 Mc/sec. Its use for our investigation was by virtue of its extremely low noise figure, at least 10 db less than the commercial receiver. Thus it made possible the detection of signals three times weaker in amplitude, and increased

59

Figure 3. 6.
The phase sensitive, 30 ∼ mixer-amplifier, according to D i c k e (D 3).

the accuracy of measurement of signals of the same size by a factor
three. The wiring diagram of the tuned phase sensitive audio-amplifier
is given in fig. 3.6. The twin T feed-back filter-stage tuned at 30∼,
is to reduce the influence of harmonics and to prevent overload of
the later stages by spurious induction from power lines etc. In the
other 6 SJ 7 tubes the 30∼ signals originating from the nuclei in the
modulated field is mixed with a 30∼ signal of about 30 V put on the
suppressor grid. The last stage is a balanced amplifier for direct current. If the output meter is fast, the time constant and the pass band
are essentially determined by the RC-circuits between the mixer and
final stage. These lead to a differential equation for the output-reading
which is similar to that of a critically damped galvanometer. The behaviour of the phase sensitive amplifier with respect to the signal-to-
noise ratio is the same as for a critically damped a.c. galvanometer
with time constant RC. The detection is sensitive both to frequency
and phase. The generator providing the 30∼ signal is represented in
fig, 3.7. It consists of a multivibrator with subsequent filters to get a
30∼ harmonic oscillation, a power amplifier to provide the current for
the modulation coils, a phase shift circuit and an amplification stage
for the beat voltage on the suppressor grids of the audio mixer, at the
same time serving for the horizontal sweep of the oscilloscope. Alter-

Figure 3.7.

The 30 ∼ generator.

natively to the multivibrator a synchronous motor was used to drive a small 30~ generator (40 Volt, 1000 Ω). The use of 30~ excluded any response of the audio-amplifier to spurious 60~ signals or harmonics thereof. Because the multivibrator was locked to the frequency of the mains, possible zero drifts, arising from slow changes in phase with respect to the mains, were excluded.

The magnet was made by the Société Génévoise. The pole pieces are schematically drawn in fig. 3. 8. The face of the pole pieces was

14 cm in diameter and the width of the gap was varied between 1.8 and 3 cm. For the first width a field of 7000 oersted was obtained at 15 amp. and 10 Volt, 11.000 oersted at 30 amp. and 16.000 oersted at 80 amp. The strongest field used was 8700 oersted. The current was supplied by two heavy duty truck batteries of 300 ampere hours each. An unsuccessful attempt had been made to regulate

Figure 3. 8.

The radiofrequency coil, in which the nuclear resonance takes place, between the pole pieces of the magnet.

the magnetic field, if the power was supplied by a generator. Since the time constant of both the magnet and the generator were of the order of one second and at the same time and unusual large periodic perturbation in the generator voltage occurred at about this frequency caused by an imperfection in the generator, the system would break into oscillations before sufficient regulation was obtained. The batteries, however, supplied a current which was very stable over intervals of ten minutes or more. Around the pole pieces two modulation coils were placed consisting of about 50 turns each. At 0.5 amp. they could provide a 30~ sweep of about 3 oersted in amplitude (6 oersted total width). The amplitude of this sweep was constant within 2% over the whole region of the gap. The main field was supposed to be made more homogeneous by the rim of 0.04 cm high and 0.8 cm wide on the edge of the pole pieces (R 8). A discussion of the actual homogeneity will be made in section 3. 5. The current through the magnet coils was measured by the voltage drop across a shunt of about 10^{-2} Ω. The

E.M.F. was balanced by a Leeds and Northrup type K potentiometer. The magnet current could be adjusted roughly by the number of 2 V cells used. Then the current passed through a manganin band of $0.2\,\Omega$, of which any part could be shorted by a sliding contact. The fine regulation was achieved by a rheostat of $5\,\Omega$, in parallel to a $0.05\,\Omega$ manganin resistance in the magnet circuit.

3.2. The radio signal caused by nuclear resonance.

We shall assume that the amplitude and frequency of the modulation sweep are so small, that the solutions obtained in chapter 2 for a time independent field H_θ remain valid. In section 3.7 we shall indicate some

Figure 3.9.

The aequivalent diagram of the nuclear resonance circuit, loosely coupled to the signal generator.

violations of the results, if the rate of change of the magnetic field is too fast. Since the condensor C_1 in fig. 3.4 provides a loose coupling, we can consider the resonance circuit, which contains the nuclei, as being driven by a constant current generator $i_0 = i\,\omega\,C_1\,V_1$, where V_1 is the voltage on R_1 (fig. 3.4). The admittance at resonance of the circuit consists only of the conductance $1/R_0 = 1/\omega\,L\,Q$. At nuclear resonance the value of L changes according to

$$\triangle L = [1 + 4\,\pi\,(\chi' - i\,\chi'')q - (1 + 4\,\pi\,\chi_0\,q)]\,L_{vac}$$
$$\triangle L \approx 4\,\pi\,(\chi' - i\,\chi'')\,q\,L \tag{3.3}$$

since χ_0 is negligibly small compared to χ' and χ''. The susceptibilities are given by (2.75) and (2.76), and q is a filling factor. If the field H_1 in the coil were homogeneous, it would be the fraction of the volume filled by the sample. The change in admittance produces a change in voltage across the coil

$$\triangle V = V - V_0$$
$$V_0 = i_0\,R_0$$
$$V = i_0\,(\frac{1}{i\,\omega\,L} + \frac{1}{R_0} + i\,\omega\,C)^{-1}$$

Making use of (3.3), of the expression for R_0 and of the fact that the change in admittance by the nuclear absorption and dispersion is small, we obtain finally:

$$\triangle V = \left(\frac{d V}{d L}\right)_{res} \triangle L = 4 \pi q \, Q \left(\chi'' + i \chi'\right) V_0 \qquad (3.4)$$

We are allowed to consider the nuclei as a voltage generator represented in fig. 3. 10. The diagram holds also for the bridge of fig. 3. 3. The bridge of fig. 3. 4 behaves as a voltage generator $\triangle V/2$ with an internal resistance $R_0/2$.

By virtue of its dependance on the susceptibility is $\triangle V$ a function of the Larmor frequency and so of the magnetic field H_0. One can plot $\triangle V$ in the complex plane. If one uses Bloch's expressions (2. 65) with a factor $\frac{1}{2}$ for the linear χ' and χ'', one finds that the locus of $\triangle V$ is a circle in the case $\gamma^2 H_1^2 T_1 T_2 \ll 1$.

On substitution of $z = \triangle \omega T_2$ we have in this case

$$(\triangle V)_{abs} = 2 \pi q \, Q \, V_0 \, M_0 \, \gamma \, T_2 \left(1 + z^2\right)^{-1} \qquad (3.5)$$

$$(\triangle V)_{disp} = 2 \pi q \, Q \, V_0 \, M_0 \, \gamma \, T_2 \, z \left(1 + z^2\right)^{-1} \qquad (3.6)$$

Figure 3. 10. The nuclear magnetic resonance is aequivalent to a voltage generator with internal impedance R_0.

If the saturation term is taken into account, on elimination of z the locus is found to be an ellipse the eccentricity of which depends on H_1. Now it has to be remembered, that the receiver detects only changes in amplitude of the input voltage. If the balance were complete, the output of a square law detector would be proportional to $|\triangle V|^2$. Under operation conditions the balance is never made complete and the situation is represented by fig. 3. 11. OA is the unbalanced signal, BO is the signal coming through the dummy circuit. If we go through the nuclear resonance by varying H_0, A goes around the circle, and the input signal of the receiver for a given value of H_0 is BC, and on the screen of the oscilloscope we see the variation of $|BC|^2$ during the sweep of the magnetic field. It has to be borne in mind that the course of C over the circle during the sweep is far from linear in H_0. The entire lower half e.g. represents the narrow part between the maximum and minimum of the dispersion curve, and C will travel much faster here than on the upper parts of the circle. On observation with the phase sensitive audio amplifier the small modulation of the field causes C to go back and forth over a small part of the circle. The amplitude of BC is then a function with a period of $1/30$ sec. The amplifier is not sensitive to the harmonics and will record only the $30 \sim$ component in the signal. In principle this can be calculated from fig. 3. 11 for any kind of balance, that is for any point B, and for any

❧❧❧

value of H_0 and H_s. Although fig. 3. 11 is drawn for the special case that the locus of $\triangle V$ is a circle, this is not essential either and the same reasoning holds for any distribution function $\varphi(\nu)$, and any value of H_1 in (2. 75). Here we shall discuss the limiting case, very well approximated in practice, that the change in voltage produced by nuclear resonance AC is small compared to BA, the signal which is left after the main part of $OA = V_0$ has been balanced by OB. The relation $|AC| << |BA|$ can be written as

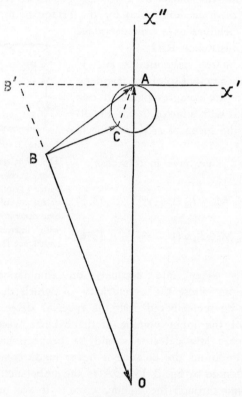

Figure 3. 11.

Diagram of the voltages in two branches of the bridge, OA and BO, and of the voltage AC, generated by the nuclear resonance.

$$\triangle V << b\,V_0 \quad (3.7)$$

Assuming a square law detector, the output will be proportional to

$$|V|^2 = b^2 |V_0|^2 + \\ + 2\,b\,\mathrm{Re}\,(V_0 \triangle V) + |\triangle V|^2 \quad (3.8)$$

Neglecting the last term, the nuclear signal is proportional to the real part of the product $V_0 \triangle V$. If B therefore lies in line with A and O, only the real part of $\triangle V$, that is only χ'' contributes to the signal. With unbalance in amplitude the absorption is measured. If B is in the position B', only χ' contributes. With unbalance in phase the dispersion is measured. To obtain the reading of the meter L, we have to look for the $30 \sim$ component in (3. 8). Assuming that the amplitude of the sweep is small compared to the line width $H_s T_2 << 1$, we can expand $\triangle V$, which via χ' and χ'' is a function of $H = H_0 + H_s \cos \omega_s t$, in a Taylor series.

$$\varDelta V(H) = \triangle V(H_0) + \frac{d\,(\triangle V)}{d\,H}\,H_s \cos \omega_s t + \tfrac{1}{2}\frac{d^2\,(\triangle V)}{d\,H^2}H_s^2 \cos^2 \omega_s t + ... \quad (3.9)$$

✦✦

The quadratic term has no components at ω_s. We neglect terms in $H_s{}^3$ and higher orders. It is readily seen from (3.4) and (3.9), that the voltage from the bridge can be described by a $30 \sim$ modulated wave

$$V_s = b\, V_0 \cos \omega_0 t\, [1 + m \cos \omega_s t] \qquad (3.10)$$

with

$$m = 4\,\pi\, q\, Q \frac{d\,\chi''}{d\,H} H_s/b \qquad (3.11)$$

Formula (3.11) holds for unbalance in amplitude. On the output meter L we then measure the derivative of the absorption function. For phase unbalance we measure the derivative of the dispersion function, and a linear combination of these derivatives, if the balance is of an intermediate type.

3.3. Limitation of the accuracy by noise.

In this experiment an essential limit for the obtainable accuracy is set by the thermodynamically determined fluctuations in voltage across the equivalent resistance of the generator of fig. 3.10. To a resistance R_0 of temperature T an effective noise voltage generator has to be attributed. The mean square voltage of this generator in a frequency range $\triangle \nu$ is

$$V_n{}^2 = I_N(\nu)\, d\nu = 4\, R\, k\, T \triangle \nu \qquad (3\ 12)$$

The precision of a measurement is limited by this fluctuating voltage and the decisive quantity is the signal to noise ratio $\sqrt{V_s{}^2/V_N{}^2}$. We shall now see what becomes of this ratio with the various methods of observation. We first suppose that the receiver has no sources of noise in itself. The voltage from the bridge can be represented by $V_s + V_n$, where V_s is given by (3.4) or by (3.10), and

$$V_n = \int_0^\infty A(\omega)\, e^{i\omega t} d\omega$$

$$|V_n|^2 = \int_0^\infty I_N(\nu)\, d\nu \qquad (3.13)$$

The problem consists in finding the low frequency part of the output spectrum after detection. We shall give the results for a square law detector in the case that the pass band of the receiver is a rectangle (outside the frequency range $\nu_0 - \frac{1}{2}\beta$, $\nu_0 + \frac{1}{2}\beta$ the gain is zero). A

❖❖❖

detailed theory of the noise with special attention to the noise in non-linear devices has been given by Rice (R 4). He also gives the results for a linear detector, which are not essentially different from the following ones. First we deal with the case that the signal is given by

$$V_s = (V_0 + \triangle V) \cos \omega_0 t \tag{3.14}$$

and the observation is made on the screen of the oscilloscope, which has a pass band larger than β, or with the meter M (see fig. 3.2), which we assume to have a rectangular pass band β_1. The time of indication of the instrument is related to β_1 and approximately $\tau_1 = 1/\beta_1$. If the balance of the bridge is complete and the signal power small compared to the noise power: $b V_0 = 0$, $\triangle V^2 << 4 R k T \beta$, the signal to noise ratio of the amplitude is $\triangle V^2 / 8 R k T \beta$ for the oscilloscope and $\triangle V^2 / R k T \sqrt{8 \beta \beta_1}$ for the slow output meter. If $\beta V_0 = 0$ and $\triangle V^2 >> 4 R k T \beta$, these ratio's become $\triangle V / \sqrt{32 R k T \beta}$ and $\triangle V / \sqrt{32 R_0 k T \beta_1}$ respectively. If there is a large unbalance $b V_0 >> \triangle V$ and also if $b^2 V_0^2 >> 4 R k T \beta$, we find

$$\left(\frac{\text{signal}}{\text{noise}}\right)_{\text{c.r.o.}} = \frac{\triangle V}{\sqrt{8 R_0 k T \beta}}$$

$$\left(\frac{\text{signal}}{\text{noise}}\right)_{\text{meter M}} = \frac{\triangle V}{\sqrt{8 R_0 k T \beta_1}} \tag{3.15}$$

If the meter M has the characteristic pass band of a critically damped galvanometer, with a period of the free system equal to τ, (3.15) goes over into

$$\left(\frac{\text{signal}}{\text{noise}}\right)_{\text{meter M}} = \frac{\triangle V \sqrt{\tau}}{\sqrt{2 \pi R_0 k T}} \tag{3.16}$$

We see that the cases with a large unbalance are the most favorable. If the observation is made with the phase sensitive audio amplifier and τ is the time necessary to take a reading, equal to the RC-value of the filter, we find for the case of large unbalance

$$\left(\frac{\text{signal}}{\text{noise}}\right)_{\text{meter L}} = \frac{V_0 m b \sqrt{\tau}}{\sqrt{4 \pi R_0 k T}} \tag{3.17}$$

We now substitute the expression for the signal $\triangle V$ (3.4) into (3.16). A limit is set to the maximum value of the occurring products $u = \chi' V_0$ and $v = \chi'' V_0$ by the relaxation time T_1. The voltage across the coil is, of course, proportional to the amplitude of the radiofrequency field H_1. If we assume the field H_1 to be uniform over the whole volume V_c of the coil, we find

$$V_0 = H_1 \omega_0 \sqrt{V_c\, L / 4\,\pi} \qquad (3.18)$$

In chapter 2 we already found that the maximum value for $\chi'\, H_1$ or $\chi''\, H_1$ is $^1/_2\, \chi_0\, H_0\, T_2^{1/2}\, T_1^{-1/2}$. Inserting this value and (3. 18) into (3. 16) we find after elimination of ω_0 and L

$$\frac{\text{signal}}{\text{noise}} = {}^1/_6\, q\, N\, Q^{1/2}\, V_c^{1/2}\, \gamma^{5/2}\, H_0^{3/2}\, T_2^{1/2}\, T_1^{-1/2}\, \tau^{1/2}\, \hbar^2\, I(I+1)(k\,T)^{-3/2}\, F^{-1/2}$$
$$(3.19)$$

Using the modulation method we have to insert (3. 11) and (3. 18) into (3. 17) and then to determine the maximum value of

$$\frac{\partial\, \chi''}{\partial\, H_0}\, H_s\, H_1$$

We find $\left(\dfrac{\partial\, \chi''}{\partial\, H_0}\, H_s\, H_1\right)_{max} = {}^1/_4\, \chi_0\, H_0\, T_1^{-1/2}\, T_2^{1/2}\, (\gamma\, T_2\, H_s)$ (3. 20)

The sweep amplitude H_s cannot be chosen larger than the line width $2/\gamma\, T_2$. If we take this value, we already should take into account higher order terms in the expansion (3. 9). So we introduce a number λ, smaller than one, and put $\gamma\, T_2\, H_s = 2\,\lambda$. We obtain for the signal to noise ratio with the modulation method

$$\frac{\text{signal}}{\text{noise}} = {}^1/_{12}\, \sqrt{2}\, \lambda\, q\, N\, Q^{1/2}\, V_c^{1/2}\, \gamma^{5/2}\, H_0^{3/2}\, T_2^{1/2}\, T_1^{-1/2}\, \tau^{1/2}\, \hbar^2\, I(I+1)(kT)^{-3/2}\, F^{-1/2}$$
$$(3.21)$$

If we use the bridge of fig. 3. 4 instead of fig. 3. 3 we have to add a factor $2^{-1/2}$ to (3. 19) and (3. 21).

Furthermore we have already added a factor $F^{-1/2}$; F is a number larger than one and is called the noise figure of the receiver. Due to the shot effect of the current in the tubes and the Brownian motion in the resistors, the receiver itself is also a source of noise. The over-all effect of this additional noise on the precision is described by the quantity F, defined by

$$\frac{\text{signal output power of generator}}{\text{noise output power of generator}} = F\, \frac{\text{signal output power of receiver}}{\text{noise output power of receiver}}$$

or F is the number, by which the absolute temperature of the internal resistance of the generator has to be multiplied, if we want to ascribe all the noise to that resistance. The factor $(kT)^{-3/2} F^{-1/2}$ in (3.19) and (3.21) must be split in two parts.

In $(kT)^{-1}$ the temperature T refers to the sample, and in $(kFT)^{-1/2}$ the effective noise temperature of the bridge is denoted by FT.

The noise figure is not a constant of the receiver, but depends on the impedance across the receiver input, and may also be a function of the frequency. It can be measured by the circuit of fig. 3.12. The tube is a

Figure 3. 12.

The noise diode. The filament is heated by a variable current, which passes through an r.f.filter. The plate current also passes through an r.f.filter. The impedance of the LC circuit is high compared to the various resistors R, parallel to it. With the switch A we can also put the bridge impedance in parallel to the tuned plate impedance. Further explanation is given in the text.

diode with tungsten filament, the temperature of which can be varied. The diode current i_d, measured by the ma-meter, is always temperature limited. We switch A into position 2 and measure the diode current necessary to double the noise power output of the receiver for various values of R. From this we obtain the noise figure as a function of R according to

$$\frac{2 e i_d R^2 \triangle \nu}{4 R k T \triangle \nu} = \frac{4 R k (FT) \triangle \nu}{4 R k T \triangle \nu} = F$$

Usually we find that the function $F(R)$ has a minimum. Then we switch A into position 1 and measure the noise figure with the bridge impedance. If the value of F so found is not close to the minimum value, the impedance of the bridge should be transformed, e.g. by another choice of the coupling condensers. The condenser C_1 is in every case adjusted for resonance. The noise figure for the pre-amplifier in combination with the bridge was found to be 2, for the National HRO 5 receiver about 12.

We now summarize the results of this section. The precision of the method is limited by the general thermodynamical fluctuations in voltage across a resistance. These could be reduced in our case by lowering the temperature of the bridge impedance. At the same time, however, care should be taken that the relative influence of noise sources in the receiver, expressed by the noise figure F, remains low. Formulae for the signal to noise ratio have been derived. It appears from (3.16) that the radio-frequency bridge must never be completely balanced; moreover, a stable complete balance would be hard to attain experimentally. With sufficient unbalance the signal to noise ratio is independent of the degree of balance b. Then the nuclear signal is detected by mixing with the main carrier rather than by a square law detector.

By observation on the audio output meter L the ratio is independent of the band width of the receiver. Increasing the precision by narrowing the pass band of the audio amplifier, is equivalent with an increase in the time required to make one measurement. The main advantage of the phase sensitive audio amplifier is not a better signal to noise ratio, for according to (3.19) and (3.21) one looses a factor $\sqrt{2}\,\lambda$ compared to the reading on meter M in the detector circuit, having the same time of indication. But the apparatus becomes less sensitive to external disturbances, as these usually do not have $30 \sim$ components. The effects of drifts in generator output and detector current are eliminated to a great extent. The zero reading is steadier. The balance of the bridge is necessary, as it is hard to find a detector, which can indicate changes of one part in 10^5 and still has a good noise figure. The balance reduces further the influence of drifts and frequency modulation in the output of the signal generator. From (3.21) we see that for the same coil the accuracy increases as $v_0{}^{7/4}$, as H_o is proportional to the resonance frequency v_0 and Q to $v_0{}^{1/2}$. Since Q is also proportional to the linear dimensions of the coil, the accuracy increases proportional to $V_c{}^{2/3}$, when the coil is enlarged.

For large coils, however, more current is needed to produce the same field density, and therefore higher demands are put on the balance. Also the field H_o has to be homogeneous over a larger area. Finally we want to stress the importance of having a good filling factor q and a high density of nuclei N.

3.4. *Measurement of the line width and relaxation time.*

In this section we assume that the magnetic field H_o is perfectly homogeneous. Suppose that we have adjusted the frequency of the signal generator and the magnetic field H_o approximately to the gyromagnetic ratio of the nuclei in the sample in the coil. On applying a modulation of sufficient amplitude to the field we shall pass through the resonance twice in each cycle. On page 71 an oscillogram of a resonance line at 29 Mc/sec of protons in 0.4 g glycerin is represented. Figure 3.13 shows the absorption, figure 3.14 the dispersion. The pictures were taken with a linear time base, while the field modulation was a 30 ~ sine function. If we also put a 30 ~ sine sweep on the horizontally deflecting plates of the oscilloscope in phase with the other sweep, we obtain a linear scale in oersted. The oscillogram in fig. 3.15 shows a resonance line in the forth and back sweep. The curves do not coincide because a small phase shift ·was left on purpose. The peculiar wiggles will be discussed at the end of this chapter. We determine the amplitude of the sweep by using a pick up coil of 1200 turns with an average area of 3 cm². The 30 ~ voltage induced in this coil, when it is put in the magnet gap is measured with a Ballantine vacuum tube voltmeter. Another way to calibrate the horizontal scale on the oscilloscope in oersted is to change the radio frequency, say, by 0.05 %. After rebalancing the bridge the resonance line appears on the screen somewhat shifted with respect to its original position. The displacement corresponds to 0.05 % of the total magnetic field.

Thus we are able to express the distance between the points of half the maximum value in oersted. The relation between this ΔH and T_2 for a damped oscillator curve is (compare section 2.6),

$$\gamma \triangle H = 2/T_2$$

and for a Gaussian $\qquad\qquad\qquad\qquad\qquad$ (3.22)

$$\gamma \triangle H = 4 \, ln \, 2/T_2$$

With the audio amplifier the line width can be measured too. A sweep of a fraction of the line width is used and the total magnet current, determining H_o, is changed in small steps. The calibration can again be made by the shift of the resonance with a small variation in the frequency. For variations of the magnetic field of less than 0.05 % a linear relation between the current and the field was found. The determination of the line width in this way was less accurate, as slight hysteresis effects can not be entirely excluded. It was only applied to wide and so usually very weak lines, which were hardly visible on the oscilloscope because of the

Figure 3. 13.

Oscillogram of the nuclear magnetic resonance absorption of
protons in glycerin at 29
Mc/sec.

Figure 3. 14.

Oscillogram of the nuclear magnetic resonance dispersion of protons in glycerin at
29 Mc/sec.

Figure 3. 15.

Oscillogram of the nuclear magnetic resonance absorption of protons in water at 29
Mc/sec. The peculiar wiggles are a transient
effect, which is discussed in section 3. 7.
Two resonances occur because a sinusoidal
sweep was used with a small phase shift,
so that the curves do not coincide. The
wiggles always appear after the sweep has
passed through resonance.

Figure 3. 16.

Oscillogram of the nuclear
magnetic resonance absorption of protons in water at
29 Mc/sec. The wiggles are
shown for a linear sweep.

noise background. In fig. 3. 17 a typical derivative absorption curve is plotted for the proton resonance in a 0.5 N solution of Fe $(NO_3)_3$. It must not be confounded with a dispersion curve! The distance $\Delta H'$ between the maximum and minimum in these curves, that is between the points of maximum slope in the original absorption curve, is related with T_2 for the damped oscillator by

$$\gamma \triangle H' = 2/\sqrt{3}\, T_2$$

and for the Gaussian by

$$\gamma \triangle H' = 2/T_2$$

(3. 23)

The actual shape of the resonance curves is discussed in detail by Pake (P 1). It cannot be easily distinguished from the experimental curves, which type of curve we have. Dispersion curves would give a better criterium. A Gaussian distribution is the most likely.

$\dfrac{\delta \chi''}{\delta H}$

0,5 N Fe(NO_3)$_3$ SOLUTION

I UNSATURATED

II SATURATED

OERSTEDT

6819   6820   6821

MAGNETIC FIELD H_o

Figure 3. 17.

The derivative of the magnetic resonance absorption of protons in a Fe $(NO_3)_3$ solution, measured with the phase sensitive audiomixer.

If the width is measured in stronger radio frequency fields a broadening of the line by saturation will set in according to (2. 63). The saturation effect enables us to measure the relaxation time T_1. The absorption curve is measured at various values of the output of the signal generator. Off resonance the detector current meter M reads proportional to this power, that is proportional to V_0^2. However, it the power of the generator has been turned up, we turn the gain of the receiver down, so that M reads its original value. In this way a direct influence of the change in the generator output on the reading of the meters M and L is eliminated. The

⋩⋩⋩

modulation H_s and the balance of the bridge are kept unchanged. From (3.8) we see that the deflection of the audio meter L will be proportional to the 30 $\sim$ modulation, and under the conditions mentioned will be proportional only to $\dfrac{\partial \chi''}{\partial H}$.

Usually we do not make use of the whole curve, but merely determine the maximum deflection in either direction. A simple calculation *) shows that the extreme values in the derivative of the absorption of the damped oscillator type (2.63) decrease with increasing H_1 yielding a deflection proportional to

$$(1 + \gamma^2 H_1^2 T_1 T_2)^{-3/2} \tag{3.24}$$

The extreme in the derivative of the dispersion should decrease only as $(1 + \gamma^2 H_1^2 T_1 T_2)^{-1}$. So for higher degrees of saturation it becomes more and more important to have pure balance, as the effect of χ' decreases more slowly than of χ''. For the Gaussian distribution it is not possible to give the decrease in the meter reading in a closed form, but the general behaviour is the same. The reading starts to decrease rapidly with increasing power, when $\gamma^2 H_1^2 T_1 T_2$ becomes of the order of unity. In any case, for the same line shapes $\dfrac{\partial \chi''}{\partial H}$ will be the same function of $\gamma^2 H_1^2 T_1 T_2$ and H_1 is proportional to the output voltage of the generator. If we plot therefore the maximum deflection of meter L against the reading of the output meter of the signal generator on a semi logarithmic scale, we obtain a series of parallel curves, which decrease rather suddenly around the value of H_1 given by $\gamma^2 H_1^2 T_1 T_2 = 1$. In fig. 3.18 some typical curves are drawn, obtained for saturation of protons in ice at various temperatures. For comparison the theoretical curve $(1 + x^2)^{-3/2}$ is indicated. Now twice the horizontal distance between the curves for different samples will give us the ratio of the products $T_1 T_2$ in these samples. And if T_2 has been measured in an independent way, we obtain the ratio of the relaxation times T_1. An absolute determination would be possible if the value of H_1 in the coil were known. Of course we know its order of magnitude from the circuit constants, but it is hard to make an estimate of the insertion and coupling losses. Therefore it was decided to make an absolute determination of the relaxation time in one substance along other lines.

---

*) Strictly speaking, formula (3.24) holds only for the case $\omega_s T_1 \ll 1$. For $\omega_s T_1 \gg 1$ the saturation is described by a different expression, which falls off somewhat slower than (3.24) with increasing H_1.

Distilled water was taken, since it was known that its relaxation time is of the order of a second, and so long enough to apply the following method.

On the screen of the oscilloscope the proton resonance was observed with a large amplitude of the sweep (about 5 oersted). The power of the generator was chosen such that no saturation occurred but was about to set in. Then the sweep amplitude was turned down to 0.5 oersted, but still the whole line, which was narrower than that value, was covered. Since the time spent at resonance was then 10 times longer, saturation would occur. After that the sweep amplitude was suddenly turned up to its original value. The height of the absorption peak immediately after this would be small, since the surplus number of protons was reduced by the preceding saturation. Exponentially the absorption peak would increase to its unsaturated value.

Figure 3. 18.

The saturation effect of the proton spin system in ice. The maximum of the derivative of χ'' is plotted, essentially against the amplitude of the alternating field H_1. The dotted curve, representing $(1 + x^2)^{-3/2}$, is indicated for comparison with theory. Data like these, in combination with data on the line width, were used to construct fig. 4. 9.

This last process was filmed with a movie camera and yielded 2.3 ± 0.5 sec. for the relaxation time in water. The same experiment was done for petroleum ether, giving 3.0 sec, and for a 0.002 N solution of $Cu\,SO_4$ in water we found 0.75 sec. All other relaxation times were measured relative to these values.

3. 5. The inhomogeneity of the magnetic field.

It turned out that in many substances, especially in liquids and gases, the measured line width was caused by the inhomogeneity of

⤓⤓

the field. The coil with sample was moved around in the magnet gap until the narrowest line was obtained. The best spot in our magnet appeared to be closer to the edge than to the centre, and there is reason to believe that the inhomogeneity is not so much caused by the geometrical conditions, as by inhomogeneities in the iron pole pieces. The best condition obtained was an inhomogeneity over the region of the sample of 0.12 oersted in a total field of 7000 oersted, and an inhomogeneity of 0.015 oersted in a field of 1100 oersted. This latter field was used for proton resonances at 4.8 Mc/sec. All lines taken in this spot in the gap, which are wider than these limits, show of course their real width. There are reasons to believe that the line width, e.g. of water, is still much narrower than 0.015 oersted.

Figure 3. 19.

The absorption of protons in water in an inhomogeneous field, as observed on the screen of an oscilloscope.

a. Unsaturated.
b. Partial saturation. The dip disappears in about the relaxation time.
c. Partial saturation over a larger region. Where the residual sweep went slow and reversed, the saturation is more complete.

The experimental results and the theory of the line width will be further discussed in the following chapter. Here we must consider, what happens to the saturation experiment, when we are forced to measure the resonance in an inhomogeneous field which determines the line shape. First we shall describe an experiment, that was of „historical interest" in the discovery of the narrow resonance lines. Suppose we have a water sample in a rather inhomogeneous field, so that the line width is two oersted. The sweep amplitude is originally turned off and the system of those nuclei, which are at resonance, is saturated. If one then suddenly turns on a sweep of 5 oersted, one sees a "hole" in the resonance line, which disappears in about 2.3 sec, the relaxation time (fig. 3. 19 b). One can also leave a small residual sweep and saturate the spin system over a somewhat broader range of the inhomogeneous field (fig. 3. 19c). The little dips indicate more saturation at the points where the sweep goes slower and reverses, that is where the nuclei are longer at resonance.

For the measurement of the relaxation time by the decrease of $\left(\frac{\partial \chi''}{\partial H}\right)_{max}$ we must distinguish three cases.

a. $\triangle h \ll H_s \ll 1/\gamma T_2$. Here $\triangle h$ is a measure for the inhomogeneity of the field which is described by the distribution function $h(\nu)$. In this case we can consider $h(\nu)$ as a δ-function and the considerations of the preceding section with formula (3.24) are valid.

b. $H_s \ll 1/\gamma T_2 \ll \triangle h$. As here the total sweep is still less than the natural line width, we can integrate the result for a single line derived in the preceding section over the distribution in the field. The reading v will be proportional to

$$v \sim \int_0^\infty \frac{\partial \chi''}{\partial H} \, h(\nu') \, d\nu'$$

Remembering that $H = 2\pi\nu/\gamma$ and $\dfrac{\partial}{\partial \nu} = -\dfrac{\partial}{\partial \nu'}$ we obtain by partial integration for the deflection

$$v \sim \int_0^\infty \chi'' \frac{\partial h}{\partial \nu'} \, d\nu'$$

If $\dfrac{\partial h}{\partial \nu'}$ changes slowly over the region of the natural width we find:

$$v \sim h'(\nu) \, (1 + \gamma^2 H_1^2 T_1 T_2)^{-1/2} \tag{3.25}$$

So the signal should decrease more slowly with increasing H_1 than in case a.

c. $1/\gamma T_2 \ll H_s \ll \triangle h$.

In this case the amplitude of the sweep is large compared to the natural width. We assume for the moment, that the sweep comes back before the nuclear system has had a chance to relax $\omega_s \gg 1/T_1$. We can define an average field density as the product of the actual density and the fraction of the time, spent at resonance. We have something as is indicated in fig. 3.19c. We are going back and forth in the bottom of the hole and have to determine the $30 \sim$ component. For the sake of simplicity let us assume that the sweep has a constant velocity given by $\dfrac{\partial H}{\partial t} = H_s \, \omega_s$ and that the line shape is a rectangle with width $2/\gamma T_2$. The fraction of the time spent at resonance is then given by $1/2\pi\gamma T_2 H_s$.

Repeating an argument similar to that leading to (2.70) we find that the surplus number of nuclei over the region of the sweep is reduced by

꙼꙼꙼

a factor $1/(1 + \gamma^2 H_1^2 T_1/2 \pi \gamma H_s)$ and the deflection of the meter is proportional to

$$v \sim \frac{h'(v)}{1 + \gamma^2 H_1^2 T_1/2 \pi \gamma H_s} \tag{3.26}$$

It has been observed experimentally that the value of H_1, necessary to produce saturation, depends on the amplitude of the sweep as must be expected from (3.26). If H_s is kept constant for various samples, we obtain a set of parallel saturation curves, which should decrease as $(1 + x^2)^{-1}$.

If we plot the curves again on semi logarithmic paper, twice the horizontal distance between them gives immediately the ratio of the relaxation times T_1. If H_o is varied in order to go through the curve $h(v)$ in fig 3.19, we meet unsaturated groups of nuclei and we must "dig a hole" in the distribution $h(v)$, before we obtain the equilibrium value *).

So far we have assumed that $H_o + H_s \sin \omega_s t$ is slowly varying, so that we could make use of the stationary solution of Bloch's equations. For narrow lines this assumption is not justified. The modulation of the field should be taken into acount by considering a frequency-modulated spectrum of the radio-frequency signal.

To estimate the order of magnitude of the transient effects, which will be discussed somewhat further in section 3.7, we assume that we have only one passage of the sweep with a velocity $H_s \omega_s$. The time spent at resonance is not, as was suggested, $1/2 \pi \gamma H_s \omega_s T_2$. For if the nuclei experience a signal only during a time t', the angular frequency is not defined better than to $\triangle \omega \approx 1/t'$, and if $1/T_2 < \triangle \omega$ we should write $1/t' = \triangle \omega = \gamma H_s \omega_s / \triangle \omega$. Substituting the experimental values $H_s = 0.02$ oersted, $\omega_s = 60 \pi \sec^{-1}$ we find for protons $\triangle \omega = 550 \sec^{-1}$. Since $\gamma H_s = 600 \sec^{-1}$, the nuclei are at resonance practically during the

---

*) This „hole" effect makes it necessary to be very careful in carrying out the experiment.

If we go through the resonance too fast, in a time comparable to the relaxation time, we are always operating on the right hand side of the hole with increasing H_o and on the left hand side with decreasing H_o. So we get large readings on meter L in opposite directions depending on the sign of the variation in H_o. So we have to go very slowly, but we cannot go too slow either, because shifts in the battery current will alter the magnetic field by a few parts in a million over periods of about half a minute and so cause jumps to other places in the line.

whole sweep. The effective energy density of the field is $\varrho\,(\nu) = \dfrac{H_1^2}{8\,\pi}\,\dfrac{2\,\pi}{\triangle\,\omega}$ and the saturation should be described by a function

$$v \approx \frac{h'\,(\nu)}{1 + \pi\,\gamma^2\,H_1^2\,T_1/\sqrt{\gamma H_s\,\omega_s}} \tag{3.27}$$

which displays the same dependence on H_1 and T_1 as (3.26). We now got rid of the restriction $\omega_s \gg 1/T_1$ for $T_2 > 1/550$ sec. If this condition is not satisfied, we immediately come back to the cases a or b. The intermediate case b should occur for values of $3.10^{-4} < T_2 < 2.10^{-3}$ but experimentally it could not be distinguished from case a, which occurs for $T_2 < 3.10^{-4}$ sec.

The ratios of the relaxation times T_1 were determined with formula (3.24) for $1/\gamma\,T_2 > H_s$ and with (3.26) for $1/\gamma\,T_2 < H_s$

This method gave very satisfactory results which are shown in the graphs of chapter 4. But we cannot exclude with certainty a serious systematic error in the determination of relative relaxation times in the region of transition, for intermediate values of T_2. The error, however, is probably less than a factor 2. For in the preceding discussion we have made some drastic simplifications, that the line shape is rectangular and the sweep linear. In fact the sweep is sinusoidal and we do not have a single passing through the resonance, so that the approximation of a signal smeared out over a frequency range $\triangle\omega$ is rough. Neither did we discuss the transitions from one case to another. Furthermore we have assumed that the oscillating field H_1 has a constant amplitude over the region of the sample. At the ends of the coil, however, H_1 will certainly be smaller. For broad lines, where H_o can be considered as homogeneous, this will tend to make the saturation curves less steep, since the systems of nuclei in various parts of the sample are not saturated at the same current in the coil. If both H_o and H_1 are inhomogeneous, the situation is very complicated. Suppose that in the middle of the coil H_o has its highest value, at the ends its lowest. Then the inhomogeneity of H_1 will even influence the shape of the unsaturated line, and on saturation we cannot expect to measure a curve given by e.g. (3.25).

Experimentally we found that the saturation curves for small values of $1/T_2$ (case c) were almost parallel to those for lines with real width in case a. The small deviation would be to the other side than predicted by (3.24) and (3.27). The curves would be steeper than $(1 + x^2)^{-3/2}$. In fig. 3.20 we give a typical example. The relaxation times, obtained from these curves and many others, will be described and compared with

79

theory in the next chapter. In fig. 3. 21 the roughest set of curves which has been used in the evaluation of the data is represented, so that the reader may form his own opinion on the obtained accuracy.

Figure 3. 20.

Saturation of the magnetic resonance absorption of protons in mixtures of water and glycerin.

Figure 3. 21.

Saturation of the magnetic resonance absorption of protons in solutions of $Fe(NO_3)_3$ of various concentrations. Data like these were used to construct fig. 4. 5.

Any systematic error could be eliminated if the field were made so homogeneous, that always the real width would be measured. In the relative measurement within the group of lines wider than 0.3 oersted, we do not expect systematic deviations. These are also eliminated in comparing the lines, which are narrower than 0.01 oersted. In these cases the error arises from the inaccuracy in the calibration of the radio frequency power meter and in the decade system to reduce the output of the signal generator. According to General Radio Co. this systematic error can amount to about 20 % in power at 30 Mc/sec. Slight drifts in balance of the bridge and gain of the receiver in the time necessary to plot a curve might affect the result by 15 %. For wide lines another 10 % has to be added for inaccuracy in the determination of T_2. In the measurement of the line width we can also expect systematic errors, caused by the line shape or the finite velocity of the sweep. The noise was always less than 10 % and in most experiments less than 1 % of the reading. Since each relaxation time is determined from an entire saturation curve, accidental errors will average out to some extent. Several runs were repeated on different days. The resulting relaxation times were reproducible within 30 %.

3. 6.   Comparison with the "nuclear induction" experiment.

There has been some confusion about the question, how the method of P u r c e l l, T o r r e y and P o u n d (P 7) compares to that of B l o c h, H a n s e n and P a c k a r d (B 7), which is called the method of nuclear induction by those authors. It may be pointed out here that there is no essential difference. B l o c h c.s. pick up the nuclear signal in a separate coil, the axis of which is perpendicular to H_o and to H_1. P u r c e l l uses the same radiofrequency coil for supplying the field and picking up the signal. We have seen in chapter 2 that the nuclear resonance depends only on one rotating component of H_1. Therefore the signal picked up in any coil perpendicular to H_o will be the same. Nothing prevents us from supposing a second coil to be present in the P u r c e l l experiment, just as in B l o c h 's arrangement. In this coil are flowing two equal and opposite currents, providing a field $H_y = \frac{1}{2} H_1 \sin \omega t$ and a field $H_y = -\frac{1}{2} H_1 \sin \omega t$. Since the sum of the currents is zero, we can leave the coil out. The only advantage to pick up the signal in a separate perpendicular coil is that one has automatically achieved a balance by the geometrical arrangement. For very high values of H_1 (> 1 oersted), where B l o c h, H a n s e n and P a c k a r d carried out their experiments, this is probably the only way of attaining the required balance. They also operate, however, for the same reason as we do, with some residual unbalance. On the type of unbalance it will depend again, whether the

✦✦

real or imaginary part of the susceptibility is measured. But at very high values of H_1 the absorption goes to zero, so that one can only measure the dispersion anyhow (G 5, B 7). At these high field strenghts information about the natural line width and relaxation time can then only be obtained by making use of nonstationary conditions, in which the frequency and amplitude of the sweep are varied. Once more it may be asserted that exactly the same phenomena would occur in the Purcell experiment with the same values of the parameters.

3. 7. Transient effects.

The non-stationary conditions, caused by the finite speed of the sweep and which are made use of in Bloch's method, cause some undesirable transient effect in our arrangement. If the time spent at resonance in the course of the sweep becomes short compared to T_1 and (or) T_2, it is not permissible to solve Bloch's equations (2.59) under the assumption, that H_z is independent of time. We shall not go into the theory, but must point out that the picture of the observed proton resonance in water (figs 3.15 and 3.16) can be explained by these non-stationary conditions. The wiggles occur after having passed through resonance. At resonance all nuclei are brought in phase by the applied radio-frequency signal. When the sweep goes on, the Larmor frequency of the nuclear precession changes and the nuclear signal will beat with the applied signal, causing alternating minima and maxima. The phase angle between the beating signal after passing the resonance at $t = 0$ is given by

$$\varphi = \int_0^t \gamma \left\{ H(t) - H_0 \right\} d.t$$

For a linear sweep φ is a quadratic function of the time. The time lapse between successive wiggles varies in the predicted way as a function of the amplitude or frequency of the sweep. The amplitude of the wiggles decays, as the nuclei get out of phase with one another. The decay time is T_2 or in an inhomogeneous field $1/\gamma \Delta h$, whichever is the shortest. The decay is partly caused by the narrow pass band of the receiver, as was checked by the use of a receiver with a broad band of 100 kc/sec. It was even possible to tune the narrow band receiver to the Larmor frequency in the wiggles, so that they become more pronounced relative to the main absorption line. If $H(t)$ is an increasing function, the wiggles, always occurring after the resonance, arise from signals of higher frequency, with decreasing $H(t)$ from signals with lower frequency than the applied signal. To the observed width of the main absorption line on the oscilloscope is also set a lower limit by the time spent at resonance, as we discussed already in section 3.5. If this time is 10^{-2} sec., the measured width cannot be narrower than 100 cycles/sec. or about 0.02 oersted for protons. With the sweep $H_s = 0.02$ oersted, $\omega_s = 60\,\pi$ sec^{-1}, used in the relaxation experiments in very narrow lines, the signals get hardly out of phase before the sweep turns back, so that the measurements of T_1 are not much affected by the wiggles.

The wiggles disappear for very small amplitude or low frequency of the sweep. Furthermore the meter L is sensitive only to the 30 $\sim$ component in the energy absorption and will not be seriously affected by the transient effect of the wiggles.

CHAPTER 4.

THEORY AND EXPERIMENTAL RESULTS.

4.1. Relaxation time and line width in liquids (B 10, B 11).

4.1.1. The Fourier Spectrum of a random function.

In chapter 2 a general theory for the relaxation time was presented. In order to apply it to practical cases we have to evaluate the Fourier spectra of the functions of the position coordinates F_0, F_1 and F_2 of section 2.5.

In a liquid these functions will vary in a random fashion with time, as the particles containing the magnetic nuclei take part in the Brownian motion. The fluctuating functions $F_0(t)$, $F_1(t)$ and $F_2(t)$ satisfy the condition

$$\overline{\text{Re } F(t)} = \overline{\text{Im } F(t)} = 0 \qquad (4.1)$$

The statistical character of the motion justifies an assumption, customary in the theory of fluctuation phenomena, that

$$\overline{F(t) F^*(t+\tau)} = k(\,|\,\tau\,|\,) \qquad (4.2)$$

The left hand side is called the correlation function of $F(t)$.

The correlation function of the random function $F(t)$ is independent of t and an even function of τ. From these assumptions it follows immediately that $k(\tau)$ is real. We shall now derive briefly the relation between this correlation function and the intensity of the Fourier spectrum of $F(t)$. A very general theory of random processes has been given by W a n g and U h l e n b e c k (W 2, R 4), where the reader may find further references. Many other investigators have pointed out the connection between the spectrum and the correlation function. We shall here follow closely K e l l e r 's (K 1) argument, although there are some slight modifications, as we want to distinguish between positive and negative frequencies and our function $F(t)$ is complex. Expand $F(t)$ in a Fourier integral

$$F(t) = \int_{-\infty}^{+\infty} A(\nu) e^{2\pi i \nu t} d\nu$$

(4. 3)

$$A(\nu) = \int_{-\infty}^{+\infty} F^*(t) e^{-2\pi i \nu t} dt$$

We assume that $F(t) = 0$ for $|t| > T$, where T is a time large compared to all times in which we ever have made or shall make observations. This assumption therefore will not alter the physical results, and in the end we can get rid of it by taking the limit $T \to \infty$. Between the functions connected by the transformation of Fourier (4. 3) exists the P a r s e v a l relation

$$\int_{-\infty}^{+\infty} F(t) F^*(t) dt = \int_{-\infty}^{+\infty} A(\nu) A^*(\nu) d\nu$$

(4. 4)

With (4. 3) and our assumption we can write this in the form

$$F(t) F^*(t) = \frac{1}{2T} \int_{-\infty}^{+\infty} d\nu \int_{-T}^{+T}\int_{-T}^{+T} F(t) F^*(t') e^{2\pi i \nu (t-t')} dt dt'$$

(4. 5)

We next make the substitutions $\sigma = t$ and $\tau = t - t'$. Using the fact that $\overline{F(\sigma) F^*(\sigma - \tau)}$ is only different from zero for small values of $|\tau|$, at any rate much smaller than T, we obtain after some calculation

$$\overline{F(t) F^*(t)} = \int_{-\infty}^{+\infty} d\nu \int_{-2T}^{+2T} e^{2\pi i \nu \tau} F(\sigma) F^*(\sigma - \tau) d\tau$$

(4. 6)

$$= \int_{-\infty}^{+\infty} J(\nu) d\nu$$

with the expression for the spectral intensity

$$J(\nu) = \int_{-\infty}^{+\infty} k(\tau) e^{2\pi i \nu \tau} d\tau$$

(4. 7)

Since $k(\tau)$ is real and even, $J(\nu)$ is real and even. Because we made a distinction between positive and negative frequencies, the intensity in (4. 7) is half the value usually found in the literature. In the following discussion we shall see that $k(\tau)$ often has the form:

✦✦✦

$$k(\tau) = \overline{F(t) F^*(t)} \exp\{- \mid \tau \mid /\tau_c\} \qquad (4.8)$$

The combination of (4.7) and (4.8) yields

$$J(\nu) = 2 \overline{F(t) F^*(t)} \frac{\tau_c}{1 + 4\pi^2 \nu^2 \tau_c^2} \qquad (4.9)$$

In general we can say that $k(\tau)$ is a function which goes rapidly to zero, if $\mid \tau \mid$ exceeds a value τ_c which is characteristic for the mechanism of the Brownian motion and is called the correlation time. The general behaviour of the Fourier spectrum is therefore such that the intensity $J(\nu)$ is practically constant for low frequencies and falls off rapidly, when $2\pi\nu\tau_c > 1$. The time average $\overline{F(t) F^*(t)}$ can be replaced by the statistical average according to a general theorem from statistical mechanics.

4.1.2. *Evaluation of the relaxation time in water.*

We start out with one water molecule, surrounded, say, by carbondisulfide, which contains no nuclear magnetic moments. We assume that the rotational magnetic moments of the molecules are also zero. We want to calculate the relaxation time of one proton due to the presence of the other. The functions F consist each of a single term:

$$F_1 = \sin\vartheta \cos\vartheta \, e^{i\varphi} /b^3 \qquad\qquad F_2 = \sin^2\vartheta \, e^{2i\varphi} /b^3$$

where b is the constant distance between the two protons. The rotation of the molecule in the liquid will change the angle between the magnetic field H_o and the radius vector connecting the two protons in a random fashion.

The correlation function of the expressions F can be calculated if we adopt the same simple picture as D e b y e (D 2) did in his famous theory of dielectric absorption and dispersion, namely a rigid sphere of radius a in a medium of viscosity η and absolute temperature T. D e b y e applies to this model E i n s t e i n's theory (E 1) of the Brownian motion. In the case that no external forces besides the thermal collisions are present, the probability to find a fixed axis of the sphere in the solid angle $\sin\vartheta \, d\vartheta \, d\varphi$ is described by the ordinary diffusion equation

$$-\frac{\partial f(\vartheta, \varphi)}{\partial t} = D \, \Delta f(\vartheta, \varphi) \qquad (4.11)$$

The diffusion constant D is given by the general expression

$$D = k\,T/\beta$$

The damping constant β for the rotation of a sphere in a viscous medium was calculated by Stokes: $\beta = 8\,\pi\,\eta\,a$.

The Laplacian Δ acts only on the angle variables ϑ and φ.

A solution of (4.11) may be written in a series of spherical harmonics $Y_{l,m,}$:

$$f = \sum_{l,\,m} c_{l,\,m}\,Y_{l,\,m}\,(\vartheta,\varphi)\ e^{-\,t\,D\,l\,(l+1)/a^2}$$

At $t = 0$ the sphere is in the position $\vartheta_0,\ \varphi_0$ and $f = \delta\,(\vartheta - \vartheta_0)\,.\,\delta\,(\varphi - \varphi_0)$. From this condition we find the coefficients

$$c_{l,\,m} = Y_{l,\,m}^{*}\,(\vartheta_0,\varphi_0)\ \Big/ \int\limits_0^\pi \int\limits_0^{2\pi}\,|\,Y_{l,\,m}\,(\vartheta,\varphi)\,|^2\,\sin\vartheta\,d\,\vartheta\,d\,\varphi$$

In order to find the correlation function $\overline{F\,(0)\,F^{*}\,(t)}$ note that $F_1 = b^{-3}\,Y_{2,\,1}\,(\vartheta,\varphi)$ and $F_2 = b^{-3}\,Y_{2,\,2}\,(\vartheta,\varphi)$.

We have $b^3\,F_1^{*}\,(t) = \int\limits_0^\pi \int\limits_0^{2\pi} f\,Y_{2,\,1}^{*}\,\sin\vartheta\,d\,\vartheta\,d\,\varphi = c_{2,\,1}^{*}\,e^{-6\,D\,t/a^2}$

The average has to be taken over all possible initial positions, i.e. over ϑ_0 and φ_0.

The final result is

$$\overline{F_1\,(0)\,F_1^{*}\,(t)} = b^{-6}\ \overline{Y_{2,\,1}^{*}\,(\vartheta_0,\varphi_0)\ Y_{2,\,1}\,(\vartheta_0,\varphi_0)}\ e^{-\frac{6\,D\,t}{a^2}} = \frac{2}{15}\,b^{-6}\,e^{-t/\tau_c}$$

$$\overline{F_2\,(0)\,F_2^{*}\,(t)} = \frac{8}{15}\,b^{-6}\,e^{-t/\tau_c} \tag{4.12}$$

$$\text{with } \tau_c = 4\,\pi\,\eta\,a^3/3\,k\,T \tag{4.13}$$

The characteristic time of D e b y e τ we obtain by carrying out the same procedure for the function $\cos\vartheta = Y_{1,\,0}$

The result is

$$\tau = 4\,\pi\,\eta\,a^3/k\,T = 3\,\tau_c \tag{4.14}$$

In D e b y e's theory τ is the time in which an assembly of water molecules, originally oriented by an electric field, loses its distribution around a preferred direction by the Brownian motion, after the electric field has been switched off. In our case τ_c is the time, in which a molecule is rotated by the Brownian motion over such an angle that the relative position of the nuclei with respect to the external field and thus the functions F have changed appreciably.

Using (4.9), (4.12) and the general formula (2.53) we find for the relaxation time of a proton in a watermolecule

$$(1/T_1)_{\text{rot}} = 0.4 \left\{ \frac{\tau_c}{1 + 4\pi^2 \nu_0^2 \tau_c^2} + \frac{2\tau_c}{1 + 16 \pi^2 \nu_0^2 \tau_c^2} \right\} \gamma^4 \hbar^2 I_p (I_p + 1) b^{-6} \tag{4.15}$$

Substituting numerical values $T = 300$, $\eta = 10^{-2}$, $a = 1.5 \times 10^{-8}$, $I_p = \frac{1}{2}$ we find that $\tau_c = 0.35 \times 10^{-11}$ sec, and since $\nu_0 = 3 \times 10^7$ cycles/sec we have $2\pi\tau_c\nu_0 \ll 1$. We see from (4.15) that in this case $1/T_1$ is proportional to τ_c and we can write with (4.15)

$$(1/T_1)_{\text{rot}} = 0.9\, \gamma^4 \hbar^2 b^{-6} \tau_c \tag{4.16}$$

The value of $\tau = 3\tau_c \approx 10^{-11}$ sec is in excellent agreement with experimental data on the dielectric absorption and dispersion in water at microwave frequencies (C 5).

Next we consider the practical case that the neighbours are not CS_2 molecules, but other H_2O molecules. We can estimate the influence of the other protons on the relaxation time in the following way.

Again the Brownian motion is responsible for the Fourier spectrum, but the cause is now rather the relative translational motion of the molecules than a rotation. Let us consider the protons in the other molecules as independent of one another[1]. We ask for $\overline{F(t)\,F(t+\tau)}$ and τ_c for the protons in a spherical shell between r and $r + dr$ around the proton of which we wish to determine the relaxation process. A reasonable value for τ_c is apparently the time it takes for a molecule to travel over a distance r. For in that time the relative position and with it the spin spin interaction has changed appreciably. From the theory of Brownian motion we have the expression for the mean square displacement of a particle

$$\overline{x^2} = 2\,k\,T\,\tau_c\,/\beta \tag{4.17}$$

---

[1] It would be better to consider the molecules as independent and attribute to them a moment $2\,\mu_{\text{p}}$ if the spins are parallel, or zero if they are antiparallel, and then apply to these moments the statistical weight of the parallel and antiparallel state. The same answer would be obtained. In the preceding problem of the rotating molecule also ortho- and para- states should have been distinguished. We shall come back to this question at the end of chapter 5.

✈✈✈

where β is a damping constant. For a sphere in a viscous medium S t o k e s derived $\beta = 6 \pi \eta a$

If one prefers to use the diffusion constant $D = k T/\beta$, we find for the correlation time

$$(\tau_c)_{\text{transl.}} = \overline{x^2}/2 D = r^2/12 D \tag{4.18}$$

since r is the relative displacement of two particles in any direction.

To find $\overline{F(t) \; F(t)}$ we have to average the angular functions over the spherical shell and multiply with the number of protons in the shell as we treat them independently. Then we have to integrate over r to include all other molecules, so approximately from $2a$, the distance of closest approach, to infinity. Using again (4.9) and (2.53) we find

$$(1/T_1)_{\text{transl.}} = 1.6 \pi N \gamma^4 \hbar^2 I_p (I_p + 1) \int_{2a}^{\infty} \frac{r^2}{r^6} \left\{ \frac{\tau_c}{1 + 4 \pi^2 \nu_0^2 \tau_c^2} + \frac{2 \tau_c}{1 + 16 \pi^2 \nu_0^2 \tau_c^2} \right\} d \tag{4.19}$$

In the integral we can neglect the term with $\nu_0^2 \tau_c^2$ in the denominators, since $2 \pi \tau_c \nu_0 \ll 1$ for $r < 10^{-7}$, and the most important contribution to the integral comes from the nearest neighbours. Integration of (4.19) then simply leads to

$$(1/T_1)_{\text{transl.}} = 0.9 \pi^2 \gamma^4 \hbar^2 \eta N/k T \tag{4.20}$$

Substituting numerical values in (4.16) and (4.20), $a = 2 \times 10^{-8}$ $b = 1.5 \times 10^{-8}$, $\eta = 10^{-2}$, $N = 7 \times 10^{22}$, $\gamma = 2.7 \times 10^4$ we find

$(T_1)_{\text{rot}} = 5.2$ sec.　　　$(T_1)_{\text{transl}} = 10$ sec.　　　$T_1 = 3.4$ sec.

This value is in good agreement with the experimental value of 2.3 sec. In the case of a rotating sphere it was possible to calculate the correlation function explicitly. For the translational effect and the rotation of more complicated molecules in liquids this would be very difficult. In these cases one might assume formula (4.8) or a linear combination of them with various τ_c. The correlation time τ_c should be larger in more viscous media as the molecular motion becomes slower. In the next section we shall discuss the general relation between the relaxation and correlation times and the viscosity.

✧✧

4. 1. 3. The relation between the relaxation time, the viscosity, the correlation time and the Debye time.

There may be some doubt whether is is permissible to extend the macroscopic notions of viscosity and diffusion to regions which contain only a few atoms. The same objection can be raised against D e b y e's theory. There, as in our case, the procedure is justified by its success. Since we obtain the right order of magnitude for the relaxation time, we might even inversely use the latter to extend our information regarding the motion of the molecules. From our general considerations we would expect that the relaxation time would decrease with increasing viscosity, as long as the condition $2 \pi \nu_0 \tau_c \ll 1$ is satisfied. This is confirmed by the experimental evidence in Table I and Table II.

Table I
Relaxation time of protons at 29 Mc/sec in hydrocarbons at 20° C

	Viscosity in centipoises	Relaxation time in seconds
Petroleumether	0.48	3.5
Ligroin	0.79	1.7
Kerosin	1.55	0.7
Light machine oil	42	0.075
Heavy machine oil	260	0.013
Mineral oil	240	0.007

Table II
Relaxation time of protons at 29 Mc/sec in polar liquids at 20° C

	Viscosity in centipoises	Relaxation time in seconds
Diethylether	0.25	3.8
Water	1.02	2.3
Ethylalcohol	1.2	2.2
Acetic acid	1.2	2.4
Sulfuric acid	25	0.7[5]
Glycerin	1000	0.02[3]

The viscosities in table I were measured with a viscosimeter, (time of flow measurement), those of table II were taken from the Physikalisch Chemische Tabelle.

We also measured the relaxation time in mixtures of water and glycerin, of which the result is shown in fig. 4. 1.

The dependence of the relaxation time on the viscosity is not quite the inverse proportionality, which one might infer from (4. 16) and (4. 20). The relaxation time in glycerin is only 10^2 times smaller than in water, while the viscosity is 10^3 times larger. In the first place one can remark that in going from one substance to another the quantities a, b and N change too. The deviation in sulfuric acid can so partly be understood because the proton density in it is much smaller than in the other substances. But for the latter the density of nuclei nor the internuclear distances b change very much from molecule to molecule. The molecular

Figure 4. 1.

The relaxation time of the proton resonance at 29 Mc/sec in mixtures of water and glycerin.

diameter a changes of course, but this would cause a deviation from the inverse proportionality with η in the direction opposite to that observed. We can only say that our treatment of a molecule as a sphere with a magnetic moment in the centre becomes very crude for large molecules, each containing several protons. In the modern theory of the viscosity a concept exists, that continually transitions are made between configurations around a given molecule, which are more or less stable. The rate at which these changes in configurations take place determines our correlation time τ_c which will depend therefore in a complicated manner on the shape and size of the molecule. For the large chain-like molecules in the hydrocarbons one has furthermore the possibility of bending and twisting of a molecule, which changes the relative position of the protons in that molecule.

The reader may be reminded that similar difficulties arise in D e b y e's theory of dielectric dispersion. His time τ determined experimentally, does not always correspond to the one calculated from (4. 14). Attempts have been made to explain this deviation by taking into account the electric dipole interaction between the polar molecules and introducing different models for the electric local field. Note that glycerin which shows the largest deviation in our case, also violates D e b y e's formula (4. 14) most severely. We want to stress, however, that the D e b y e time τ and our correlation time τ_c characterize different physical processes. D e b y e's τ refers only to the orientation of the polar group in space, while for τ_c any relative reorientation between the magnetic nuclei must be considered. The following formulation then seems appropriate. The characteristic time τ of D e b y e and the correlation time τ_c in the magnetic local field spectrum are proportional in one sample. They both vary in proportion to η/T, if the temperature of the sample is changed.

The proportionality constant between τ and τ_c varies from substance to substance, depending on the detailed picture of the molecular motion in each substance, but the ratio will always be of the order of unity. For the model of a sphere in a viscous medium we have $3\,\tau_c = \tau$. Experimental values for the proportionality factor are given in section 4. 3. 1.

We can obtain a better test of the theory if we carry out measurements of the relaxation time and line width in one substance at various temperatures. We shall first describe in some detail the behaviour of T_1 and T_2, that must be expected from theory. Substitution of (4. 9) and (4. 12) into (2. 54) and (2. 53) leads to

$$1/T_1 = K_1 \left[\frac{\tau_c}{1 + 4\,\pi^2\,\nu^2\,\tau_c{}^2} + \frac{2\,\tau_c}{1 + 16\,\pi^2\,\nu^2\,\tau_c{}^2} \right] \tag{4.21}$$

$$1/T_2' = \sqrt{K_0 \int_{-1/\pi T_2'}^{1/\pi T_2'} \frac{\tau_c}{1 + 4\,\pi^2\,\nu^2\,\tau_c{}^2}\,d\nu} = \sqrt{\frac{K_0}{\pi} \arctan \frac{2\,\tau_c}{T_2'}} \tag{4.22}$$

with $$K_1 = {}^2\!/_5\,\gamma^4\,\hbar^2\,I\,(I + 1)\,b^{-6} \tag{4.23}$$

and $$K_0 = 3\,K_1 \tag{4.24}$$

It has been assumed that the averaging over ϑ could be carried out independently. Use has been made of the relations (4.12). Furthermore the formulae are written for a single relaxation time $\tau \sim c\,\eta/T$. Actually we have a distribution of relaxation times as we have seen for the translational effect in water. We should write instead of the constant c the function $c(\lambda)$ and integrate over the parameter λ. In most cases the distribution will be narrow, since only the nearest neighbours contribute strongly. Strictly speaking the constants K are functions of the temperature, as they vary with the density of the sample, but this effect

Figure 4. 2.

The theoretical behaviour of the relaxation time T_1 and T_2, which is a measure for the inverse line width.

is completely negligible. The simplifying assumptions now permit to point out clearly the general behaviour of T_1 and T_2, which are plotted as a function of τ_c in fig. 4.2. Here T_2 is defined by (2.58).

For $4\,\pi^2\,\nu^2\,\tau_c^2 \ll 1$, T_1 is inversely proportional to τ_c and thus to η/T, and for $4\,\pi^2\,\nu^2\,\tau_c^2 \gg 1$ directly proportional. The plot on a double logarithmic scale therefore shows two straight lines making angles of $45°$ and $135°$ degrees with the x-axis.

In the transition region $(4\,\pi^2\,\tau_c{}^2\,\nu^2 \approx 1)$ T_1 has a minimum value

$$(T_1)_{min} = {}^4/_8\,K_1\,\tau_c \qquad (4.25)$$

for
$$\tau_c = {}^1/_2\,\sqrt{2}\,\pi\,\nu_0$$

The quantity T_2' is a monotonic decreasing function of τ_c and reaches an asymptotic value

$$(1/T_2')_{asymptotic} = \sqrt{{}^1/_2\,K_0} \qquad (4.26)$$

for very long correlation times. This value is of course exactly the same as the one we calculated for the static case (2.36) where the nuclei are at rest. For $\tau_c \ll (T_2')_{asymptotic}$, T_2' is inversely proportional to τ_c. The horizontal distance between the points, where T_1 and T_2 bend over respectively, is given by the ratio $2\,\pi\,\nu_0\,(T_2')_{asymptotic} \approx H_0/H_{loc}$. For $4\,\pi^2\,\nu^2\,\tau_c{}^2 \ll 1$, T_1 and T_2' are proportional and from (4.21) and (4.22) we find for the proportionality constant

$$T_2' = {}^1/_2\,\pi\,T_1 \qquad (4.27)$$

The line width is given by (2.58) with one of the relations (3.22) or (3.23). For $4\,\pi^2\,\nu_0{}^2\,\tau_c{}^2 \gg 1$ we have

$$T_2 \approx T_2' \qquad (4.28)$$

for $4\,\pi^2\,\nu_0{}^2\,\tau_c{}^2 \ll 1$ we have with (4.27)

$$T_2 = 0.85\,T_1 \qquad (4.29)$$

We must not attach too much weight to this particular ratio, for about the limits in the integral in (4.22) we only know that they must be of the order of magnitude of the line width expressed in cycles/sec. It might be better to take the limits as $\pm\,1/\pi\,T_2$ instead of $\pm\,1/\pi\,T_2'$. This would not make any difference for long τ_c's, and does not affect the order of magnitude for the region where T_1 and T_2 are proportional. We shall see in the next paragraphs that the experimental ratio between T_1 and T_2 is close to the value predicted by (4.28) and (4.29). On this basis the resonance line in water e.g. with $T_1 = 2.3$ sec. should be very narrow indeed. The width should be of the order of one cycle or about 10^{-4} oersted. The experimental width is then, of course, determined by the inhomogeneity in H_0 as we have already pointed out several times.

❖❖

4. 1. 4. *Experimental results in ethyl alcohol and glycerin between* + 60° C *and* —35° C.

In order to vary the temperature of the sample in the radiofrequency coil, copper tubing (3mm inside diameter) was soldered around the grounded shield of the radiofrequency coil (see fig. 3. 8). To obtain low temperatures acetone, cooled by dry ice, could flow through the tubing from a container, which was placed above the magnet, under the influence of the gravitational force. This acetone was not in direct contact with the dry ice. For dissolved CO_2 would be set free, when the acetone was warmed up in passing through the narrow tubing. This would prevent a regular flow. The apparatus in the magnet gap and all other cold parts were thermally insulated with glass wool and asbestos paper. The temperature was measured by a copper-constantan thermo-element. One contact point was brought in the liquid through the small cork stop closing the thin walled glass tube which contained the sample. There was no trouble of pick-up of radio frequencies, since the coupling between the leads of the thermo-element and the coil was very small indeed, as the contact point was kept well outside the volume of the coil. The other contact of the element was put in melting ice. The thermo — E.M.F. was measured with a Leeds & Northrup type K potentiometer. The element was calibrated at + 100° C, 0° C and —78° C, which checked with the calibration data given in the Handbook of Chemistry and Physics, so that this table was used. The temperature of the sample could be varied by changing the flow of the cooling liquid. The temperature remained constant to within 0.5° C during the determination of each saturation curve. The balance of the bridge was also stable, once thermal equilibrium had been established. To cover the range of higher temperature, the container was filled with iced water or hot water.

The variation of the viscosity with temperature was taken from the Physikalisch-Chemische Tabelle. The data obtained with ethylalcohol at two frequencies are shown in fig. 4. 3. The variation of the relaxation time with viscosity is inversely proportional. The line drawn through the points makes an angle of 135° with the x-axis. Although the variation in the viscosity is not large, the points clearly indicate the theoretical behaviour, to be expected for short τ_c. The real line width could not be measured. The limit set by the inhomogeneity of the field is 0.015 oersted at 4.8 Mc/sec. According to theory the line width should be much narrower than this. As was pointed out in chapter 3, any systematic errors in the relative determination of T_1 cancel out in this case. More interesting are the results for glycerin shown in fig. 4. 4. The freezing point of this sub-

🙂🙂🙂

stance is 18° C, but it usually gets supercooled and very high viscosities are obtained at low temperature, where the substance becomes almost glasslike. The experimental points show that we have reached the region where $2 \pi \nu_0 \tau_c > 1$. The drawn lines are theoretical curves. The observed minima are somewhat flatter and on the low temperature side the points do not quite fit a 45° line. This can, at least in part, be explained by a distribution of correlation times τ_c, rather than the single value to which

Figure 4. 3.

The relaxation time of the proton resonance in ethyl alcohol between 60° C and — 35° C. The straight line makes an angle of 45° degrees with the negative x-axis.

the theoretical curves pertain. It would be interesting to extend the measurements to lower temperatures to get more information about this distribution. The shift of the minimum with frequency is somewhat less than predicted by (4. 25). We find a factor 4 instead of 6. On the low temperature side the relaxation time should be proportional to ν_0^2. Instead of a factor 36 we find a factor 14. Again this deviation can, at

꒚꒚

least partly, be understood by remarking that (4. 25) holds only in case of a single correlation time, or if one wishes, of a single correlation function. The data on the line width are plotted in the same diagram with the aid of formula (3. 22) for a Gaussian curve.

At room temperature the line is narrower than the inhomogeneity of the external field. Extrapolation of the dotted line towards higher temperatures gives the ratio $T_1/T_2' = 1$. In the region where T_1 is proportional to the viscosity and T_2 inversely proportional, the saturation of the line

Figure 4. 4.

The relaxation time and the line width of the proton resonance in glycerin between 60° C and −35° C. The lines, drawn through the experimental points, have the theoretical form of fig. 4. 2.

always occurs at the same output power of the generator, that is at the same density of the applied radio frequency field, as the product T_1T_2 is constant. From the viscosity, measured at 20° C, it followed that the glycerin used in the experiment was not pure and probably contaminated with 2 % water. Experiments carried out with mineral oil gave similar results both for the relaxation time and line width.

4. 1. 5. *The influence of paramagnetic ions.*

So far we have considered the dependence of the relaxation time on τ_c. It is also possible, however, to bring about changes in the quantities K_1 and K_0 in (4. 21) and (4. 22) by mixing the substance with paramagnetic ions. From (4. 23) and (4. 24) we see that the large γ-values of the electronic moments will enhance the values of K_1 and K_2. The larger interaction of the nuclear moment with the electronic moment will shorten the relaxation time and enhance the line width, τ_c remaining constant. Let us consider an aqueous solution of ferric nitrate. We can calculate the influence of the Fe^{+++} ions in the same way as we did, when we estimated the contribution of the protons in other molecules to the relaxation time in pure water. An adapted formula (4. 20) would read

$$1/T_1 = 12\,\pi^2\,\gamma_p{}^2\,\gamma_{ion}^2\,\hbar^2\,S_{ion}\,(S_{ion}+1)\,N_{ion}\,\eta/5\,k\,T \qquad (4.30)$$

This applies for ions of the iron-group, which are of the "spin-only" type. For others we should replace $\gamma_{ion}^2\,\hbar^2\,S_{ion}\,(S_{ion}+1)$ by μ_{eff}^2.

Of course we should add to (4. 30) the contribution of the protons in the solution, which in pure water are solely responsible for the relaxation time. But as γ_{ion}^2 is about 10^6 times larger than $\gamma_p{}^2$, the influence of the paramagnetic ions is predominating even in a concentration of 10^{-3} N. or 10^{18} ions/cc. According to (4. 30) the relaxation time should be inversely proportional to the concentration and to the square of the magnetic moment of the paramagnetic ions. In fig. 4. 5 the results for three ions are given. It appears that the curves, also to the absolute magnitude, can be well represented by (4. 30). Only for very low frequencies there seems to be a deviation towards longer relaxation times. This is all the more remarkable since the straight lines finally must bend over to the left to the asymptotic value of 2.3 sec. in pure water. We do not know if the effect is real. It certainly seems too big for a systematic error. We would like to point out that (4. 30) certainly needs some correction. For while the motion of a watermolecule relative to the ion is still given by (4. 17) and (4. 18), where a is the radius of the watermolecule, the distance of closest approach is determined by the radius of the ion and its hydratation. We must insert a correction factor a/b. It is very hard to estimate correctly the motion of a watermolecule in the dipole atmosphere around an ion. But if there is an effect from the hydratation, it should become more pronounced at small concentrations.

Furthermore we should take into account that the correlation time in the local field spectrum is not solely determined by the molecular motion in the liquid, but also by changes in quantisation of the electronic spins, which possibility was already indicated in (2. 42). The characteristic time for this latter process is not known experimentally, as the paramagnetic electronic relaxation times $\varrho/2\pi$ in solutions are short, of the order of 10^{-10} sec. [1]). This implies that in the derivation of (4. 30) we should have used for τ_c the constant ϱ instead of (4. 18) for values of

SATURATION OF PARAMAGNETIC SOLUTION

x Cu^{++}
o Fe^{+++}
△ Er^{+++}

Figure 4. 5.

The relaxation time of the proton resonance in aqueous solutions of paramagnetic salts. The lines, drawn through the experimental points, make angles of 45° with the negative X-axis.

r, where τ_c would become larger than ϱ. This reduces only the influence of the ions which are rather far away, so that this correction is not

[1]) One might be tempted to calculate ρ in the same way as we did for the nuclear relaxation time. However, more important than the magnetic interaction between the spins will be the electric interaction in the polar liquid via the spin-orbit coupling. The only experimental information, known to the author, comes from Z a v o i s k y (Z 1).

✢✢

important. The inverse proportionality with μ_{eff}^2 is rather well realised for some ions, and completely violated for others (Ni^{++}, and especially Co^{++} and $Fe(CN)_6^{---}$), as is shown in Table III.

TABLE III.

Ion	μ_{eff} in Bohr magnetons from relaxation experiments	μ_{eff} in Bohr magnetons from susceptibility measurements
Er^{+++}	9.5	9.4
Fe^{+++}	6.3	5.9
Cr^{+++}	4.7	3.8
Cu^{++}	2.3	1.9
Ni^{++}	2.1	3.2
Co^{++}	1.3	4.5—5.3
$Fe(CN)_6^{---}$	0.12	2.4

The second column is computed with (4. 30) from measurements of the nuclear relaxation time in solutions of known concentration. The values in the last column were taken from G o r t e r (G 3).

They were obtained from the measurement of the static susceptibility of solutions (comp. V 1). The value for $Fe(CN_6)^{---}$ was taken from measurements on solid $K_3Fe(CN)_6$ (J 1). The large deviations for the last three ions can be understood, because nondiagonal elements [1]) contribute greatly to the magnetic moment of these ions. With these elements components of the local field spectrum are connected, which have a higher frequency than $\nu_0 + 1/\tau_c$, where $1/\tau_c$ is the limit where the local spectrum caused by the Brownian motion drops off rapidly. Thus these non-diagonal elements do not contribute to the nuclear relaxation mechanism, and the μ_{eff} for this process is correspondingly smaller. The extremely small influence of $Fe(CN)_6^{---}$ is probably partly caused by the six CN groups around the iron atom, so that the b is very large. For variations of b for the various ions have not been taken into account in Table III.

Finally we may ask what the influence can be of oxygen gas dissolved in water. The magnetic moment of O_2 is 2.8. The maximum concentration of dissolved O_2 in water at room temperature under 18 % of the atmospheric pressure is 1.5×10^{17} molecules/cc. The relaxation time, due to O_2 alone, could not be smaller than 2.5 sec. The relaxation time in water is therefore determined by the neighbouring protons and the dissolved

---

[1]) For Co^{++} and $Fe (CN)_6^{---}$ even important deviations from C u r i e's law have been found.

100

oxygen. In the determination of the absolute value of the relaxation time (see chapter 3) distilled water was used. As the distillation was not done in vacuo, we have no guarantee that for pure water the relaxation time is not somewhat longer.

We now consider the line width in the solutions. As the correlation time τ_c in paramagnetic solutions is essentially the same as in water and thus $4\pi_0 \nu_0^2 \tau_c^2 \ll 1$, we expect that T_2 is proportional to T_1. This is confirmed by the experimental result in fig. 4. 6. The line width, measured

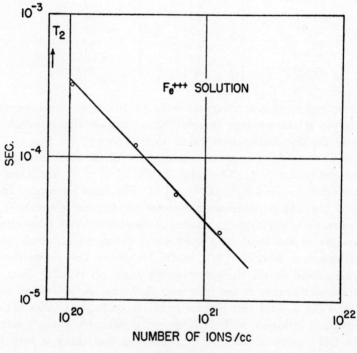

Figure 4. 6.

The line width of the proton resonance in aqueous solutions of $Fe(NO_3)_3$. The quantity T_2 is inversely proportional to the line width, which appears to be proportional to the concentration.

between the points of maximum slope in an assumed Gaussian, is $2/\gamma\, T_2$, and is proportional to the concentration. For small concentrations the width is again too narrow to be measured. Comparison of fig. 4. 5 and 4. 6 yields $T_2 = 1/2\, T_1$ or $T_2' = 2/3\, T_1$. The same ratio was found for Cu^{++} solutions and is in good agreement with the value found in glycerin.

It may be well to point out here that the proton resonance in paramagnetic solutions appears to be shifted, because the field inside the sample is different from the field elsewhere in the gap. The microscopic field inside the sample at the position of the protons always determines the position of the proton resonance. We are interested in the field produced by all paramagnetic ions at the position of a proton and not of all but one at the position of another ion. It is not permissible to put the macroscopic $\vec{H}$ inside the sample into the resonance condition (1.7). One has to take the average microscopic field at the position of the protons. At the same time we might mention another factor which changes slightly the magnetic field experienced by a nucleus, namely the diamagnetism of the surrounding electrons. This effect has been calculated by R a b i and coworkers and is very small for light elements (K 12).

4. 1. 6.   *The resonance of F^{19} and Li^7 in liquids.*

To compare the resonances of F^{19} and H^1 in a liquid compound, a "Freon", $CHFCl_2$, monofluoro-dichloro-methane, was condensed in a glass tube and sealed off. Both the H^1 and F^{19} resonance were narrower than the inhomogeneity in the field. The total intensity of the two lines was the same (within 15 %) so that it was confirmed that F^{19} has the same spin as the proton. The relaxation times were 3.0 sec. for H^1 and 2.6 sec. for F^{19}. The γ_F is 6.5 % smaller than γ_P, but the F^{19} nucleus experiences a somewhat larger local field as its nearest neighbour is the proton in the same molecule, while the proton has in turn the F^{19} nucleus. We should expect on this basis the relaxation times to be the same, as is confirmed within the experimental error.

Experiments were also carried out in solutions of KF. Since the signal to noise ratio drops proportional to the number of nuclei per cc, only very concentrated solutions could be investigated to obtain a sufficiently intense F^{19} resonance. Again the resonance lines are narrow. The result for the relaxation times is shown in fig. 4. 7. The decrease in the proton relaxation time can be explained by the increase in viscosity of the concentrated solution. The much more pronounced decrease for fluorine may be an indication that the motion of these ions is more quenched, when one comes very close to the transition point, where the solution changes into the solid hydrate $KF.2H_2O$. A more careful study of the nuclear relaxation might give information about the character of this, and other, transitions. Anticipating the results for solids we can say that in the crystalline $KF.2H_2O$ the lines are wide and that we are in the region where $4\pi^2 \tau_c^2 \nu_0^2 \gg 1$.

An interesting substance is also BeF_2, which can be mixed with water in any proportion. For high concentrations the substance becomes very viscous, and finally goes over into the glasslike, amorphous BeF_2, when no water is present. Preliminary experiments showed that the behaviour of both the proton and the fluorine resonance in $Be\ F_2 + H_2O$ is similar to that of the proton resonance in glycerin. With increasing viscosity of the mixture the relaxation time first drops to about 10^{-3} sec., then rises

Figure 4. 7.

The relaxation time of the proton and fluorine resonance in aqueous solutions of K F of various concentrations.

again to 0.2 sec in pure BeF_2. The line width measured between the points of maximum slope increases from very small values to about 10 oersted in pure BeF_2.

Experiments on the Li^7 resonance were carried out at 14.5 Mc/sec

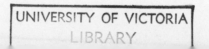

TABLE IV.

Substance	Number of Li atoms	Relaxation time in seconds	
	Number of H atoms	for Li^7	for H^1
$LiCl + H_2O$	5.8	1.75	0.4
$LiNO_3 + H_2O$	14	2.7	1.1
$LiNO_3 + H_2O + Fe(NO_3)_3$	8	0.11	0.002^3
$LiCl + H_2O + CrCl_3$	6.5	0.24	0.009^5
$LiCl + H_2O + CuSO_4$	6.6	0.18	0.01^3

in solutions of LiCl and $LiNO_3$. Table IV gives some results. For the solutions without paramagnetic ions the decrease in relaxation time of the proton resonance compared to pure water can be explained by an increase in viscosity of the concentrated solutions. The relaxation time for Li^7 in this case is somewhat longer. The ratio of the local field spectra is given by

$$\frac{\text{Spectral intensity at } Li^7 \text{ nucleus}}{\text{Spectral intensity at proton}} = \frac{(T_1 \gamma^2)_p}{(T_1 \gamma^2)_{Li^7}}$$

Since $\gamma_p^2 / \gamma_{Li}^2 = 6.6$, the local field has a somewhat higher intensity at the Li-nucleus. The cause could be the slower motion of the largely hydrated Li-ion. A more likely explanation however, is, as we shall see later, that the intensity of the magnetic local field is the same, or even smaller but that there is a contribution to the relaxation process from the quadrupole moment of Li^7, which has a spin $I = {}^3/_2$.

The influence of paramagnetic ions is much smaller on Li^7 than on the protons. In the first place the local field spectrum at the Li^7 nucleus will be smaller because the repulsion of two positive ions will make it less likely for them to come close together, and then they have to compete with the quadrupole transitions (cf. chapter 5). At the conclusion of this paragraph we direct the attention of the reader to the results found by other investigators (B 2, B 7, R 5), which seem to be in agreement with the general ideas, here proposed. Especially we might mention the experiment in liquid hydrogen by R o l l i n (R 6).

4. 2. The relaxation time and line width in gases.

4. 2. 1. Hydrogen.

The only experiment of nuclear magnetic resonance (P 6) in gases which has been reported was performed with hydrogen gas at room temperature between 10 and 30 atmospheres of pressure. The accuracy

✦✦

was poor, as the density of the nuclei is low. It was found that the line is narrow (< 0.15 oersted) and that the relaxation time at 10 atmospheres $T_1 \approx 0.015$ sec. with an indication that T_1 increases with increasing pressure. We shall now investigate what the theory predicts for this case.

The local field at the position of a proton in an H_2-molecule in a volume of hydrogen gas consists in the first place of the contribution connected with the rotational moment $\vec{J}$ of the molecule and the magnetic moment of the other proton. According to P a u l i's exclusion principle the spins of the two protons can only be parallel, if the electronic wave function is antisymmetric (J odd, orthohydrogen), and only anti-parallel, if the electronic wave function is symmetric (J even, parahydrogen). The transitions from the ortho- to the para-state in hydrogen gas are extremely rare. Furthermore, if the system is in thermal equilibrium at room temperature, 13 % of the H_2 molecules have $J = 0$, 66 % have $J = 1$, 12 % have $J = 2$ and 9 % have $J = 3$. We ignore for the sake of the simplicity transitions from $J = 1$ to $J = 3$. We assume that the rotational angular momentum of orthohydrogen is a constant of the motion. The total nuclear spin $I = I_1 + I_2$, $I = 0$ for parahydrogen, $I = 1$ for orthohydrogen. Only orthohydrogen will show nuclear reso-nance. At room temperature equilibrium the ratio of molecules in ortho- and para-states is as $3 : 1$. So the total intensity of the nuclear magnetic absorption line is proportional to $\frac{3}{8} NI(I + 1)$. This is equal to $(\frac{1}{2} \cdot \frac{3}{2})N$. Thus the total intensity of the line of orthohydrogen is the same as if all N protons were uncoupled in hydrogen atoms.

If the molecule is placed in a strong magnetic field, in zero approxima-tion not only I and J, but also m_I and m_J are constants of the motion. We first consider the interaction of the nuclear spin with the rotational moment. The perturbation term in the Hamiltonian is given by

$$H_{op} = \gamma \hbar H' \vec{I} \vec{J}$$

$$= \frac{1}{2} \gamma \hbar H' \{(I_x + i I_y)(J_x - i J_y) + (I_x - i I_y)(J_x + i J_y)\} + \gamma \hbar H' I_z J_z$$

$$(4.31)$$

From R a b i's experiments (K 3) follows the value of H'; the magnetic field at the position of the protons produced by the rotation of the molecule is 27 oersted. With (4.31) we can once more repeat the reasoning explained in sections 2.4 and 2.5 in order to calculate the relaxation time. If the quantisation of J were fixed, that is if m_J did not change during collisions, we would have no transitions in m_I. For the first two terms on the left hand side in (4. 31), which have non-diagonal elements in m_I, involve also a change in m_J. But the collisions in the gas will change m_J and we can assume that after each collison m_J has equal chance for any of its $2J + 1$ values. As the distribution of the collisions in time of a given molecule, measured from the time of the preceding collision, is given by $\frac{1}{\tau_c} \exp{- t/\tau_c}$, where τ_c is the mean collision time in the gas, we have a Fourier spectrum for m_J and thus for $J_x - i\,J_y$. The intensity of the spectrum of the latter is with (4. 9)

$$J(\nu) = \frac{4\,J(J+1)}{3} \frac{\tau_c}{1 + 4\,\pi^2\,\nu^2\,\tau_c{}^2} \tag{4. 32}$$

From this and (4. 31) we obtain a relaxation time

$$1/T_1 = \frac{2\,\tau_c}{1 + 4\,\pi^2\,\nu_0{}^2\,\tau_c{}^2}\,H'^2\,\gamma_p{}^2\,\frac{J(J+1)}{3} \tag{4. 33}$$

with $$\tau_c = 1{,}4/\,v\,\sigma\,N \tag{4. 34}$$

The number of molecules per cc, proportional to the pressure, is denoted by N, σ is the collision cross section, v is the average velocity of the molecules.

To (4. 33) we have to add the contribution of the spin-spin interaction, which is represented by the perturbation term

$$H_{op}'' = \frac{-\gamma_p{}^2\,\hbar^2}{r^3}\left[3\,(\vec{I_1}\cdot\vec{n})(\vec{I_2}\cdot\vec{n}) - \vec{I_1}\cdot\vec{I_2}\right] \tag{4. 35}$$

where $\vec{n}$ is the unit vector pointing from one proton to the other, and r is the distance between them. The expression (4. 35) can be transformed to one which only contains constants and the operators $\vec{J}$ and $\vec{I} = \vec{I_1} + \vec{I_2}$,

$$H_{op}'' = \gamma_p{}^2\hbar^2\frac{1}{r^3}\frac{I(I+1) + 4\,I_1\,(I_1+1)}{(2\,I-1)(2\,I+3)(2\,J-1)(2\,J+3)}\left[3\,(\vec{I}\cdot\vec{J})^2 + {}^3/_2\,\vec{I}\cdot\vec{J} - \vec{I}^2\cdot\vec{J}^2\right] \tag{4. 36}$$

In order to find the contribution of this interaction to the relaxation process, we have to write the operator between square brackets in the

m_I, m_J representation. R a b i and collaborators (K 4) found that this operator is equal to

$$\tfrac{1}{2}\,[3\,J_z^2 - J(J+1)]\,[3\,I_z^2 - I(I+1)] + \qquad \triangle\,m_I = \triangle\,m_J = 0$$

$$+ \tfrac{3}{4}\,[J_z\,(J_x + i\,J_y) + (J_x + i\,J_y)\,J_z]\,[I_z\,(I_x - i\,I_y) + (I_x - i\,I_y)\,I_z]$$
$$- \triangle\,m_I = + \triangle\,m_J = 1$$

$$+ \tfrac{3}{4}\,[J_z\,(J_x - i\,J_y) + (J_x - i\,J_y)\,J_z]\,[I_z\,(I_x + i\,I_y) + (I_x + i\,I_y)\,I_z]$$
$$\triangle\,m_I = - \triangle\,m_J = 1$$

$$+ \tfrac{3}{4}\,(I_x + i\,I_y)^2\,(J_x - i\,J_y)^2 \qquad \triangle\,m_I = - \triangle\,m_J = 2$$

$$+ \tfrac{3}{4}\,(I_x - i\,I_y)^2\,(J_x + i\,J_y)^2 \qquad - \triangle\,m_I = \triangle\,m_J = 2$$

$$(4.\,37)$$

The matrix elements can be written down immediately with the rules of matrix multiplication and the expressions (1,1), (1,2) and (1.3). The matrix elements of (4. 37) with $\Delta m_I = 1$ and 2, combined with the components at ν_0 and $2\nu_0$ of the frequency spectrum of the corresponding terms in m_J give an expression for $1/T_1$, which must be added to (4. 33).

We write down the final result, first derived by S c h w i n g e r for the case realized in practice that τ_c is short compared to the Larmor period $1/\nu_0$.

$$(1/T_1)_{H_2 - \text{gas}} = 2\,\tau_c\,\gamma_p^2\,\left[\frac{1}{3}H''^2 J(J+1) + 3\,H''^2\,\frac{J(J+1)}{(2J-1)(2J+3)}\right]$$

$$(4.\,38)$$

where $H'' = \dfrac{1}{r^3}\,\tfrac{1}{2}\gamma\,\hbar$ is the effective field from one proton at the position of the other. From R a b i's experiments (K 3) follows $H'' = 34$ oersted. In (4. 38) we have already asumed $4\,\pi^2\,\nu_0^2\,\tau_c^2 \ll 1$. This is always fulfilled under practical conditions. The opposite case $4\,\pi^2\,\nu_0^2\,\tau_c^2 \gg 1$ would occur at pressures of 1 mm Hg or less, where the signal is much too small to be detected. From (4. 38) and (4. 34) it follows that the relaxation time T_1 is proportional to the pressure. Substituting numerical values $\gamma_p = 2.7 \times 10^4$, $J = 1$, $\tau_c = 10^{-11}$ sec. (Handbook of Chemistry and Physics) for a pressure of 10 atmospheres, we find $T_1 = 0.03$ sec, which is in agreement with the experimental value.

The line width can be calculated on similar lines as we did in chapter 2 from (4.31) and (4.32). As in liquids we find again that T_2 is of the same order as T_1, so that the resonance line should be very narrow. As T_2 is proportional to T_1, the line width should be inversely proportional to the pressure. We can speak of "pressure-narrowing" of the nuclear resonance line in H_2-gas.

The conclusion is: The magnetic interactions in the H_2-molecule give rise to a fine structure of the radiofrequency spectrum in R a b i's molecular beam method (K 3). Combined with the collisions in the gas sample for pressures > 10 mm Hg, as used in P u r c e l l's method, they give rise to a relaxation mechanism and the local fields average out to a single very narrow line.

We have not considered the influence of the other molecules during a collision on the relaxation time. In the next paragraph we shall see, that this effect can usually be neglected in H_2-gas.

4.2.2. Helium.

An entirely different state of affairs occurs in the interesting case of He³ gas. The atoms are in an S-state. The only perturbation is brought about during the collisions by the nuclear magnetic moment of the colliding atom. Unlike in hydrogen, here the influence of the other molecules is the only effect. Suppose that the He³ nucleus has the set of eigenfunctions ψ_n in the constant field H_0. We ask for the chance that the perturbation by a collision brings the system from the initial state i with energy E_i to the final state f with energy E_f. The perturbation method, which may be applied, if the chance in one collision is small compared to unity, gives for the probability to find the system in state f after the collision

$$w_f = \frac{\sin^2 \frac{E_f - E_i}{\hbar} t}{(E_f - E_i)^2} \left| (f \mid H_{op} \mid i) \right|^2 \tag{4.39}$$

We cannot say precisely, what is going on during the collision. But the order of magnitude of the matrix element of the perturbation operator between the initial and final state will be the same as that of the interaction energy $\approx \gamma_1 \gamma_2 \hbar^2 d^{-3}$. The colliding particles have magnetogyric ratio's γ_1 and γ_2 and d is the distance of closest approach between the moments during the collision. The time t, during which a strong inter-

✧✧

action takes place, is probably $\approx 10^{-15}$ sec, at any rate $t \ll \hbar/E_f{-}E_i \approx$ 10^{-8} sec. We can therefore write instead of (4. 39)

$$w_f = \gamma_1{}^2\,\gamma_2{}^2\,\hbar^2\,t^2\,d^{-6} \tag{4. 40}$$

If v is the relative velocity of the colliding particles, we have $t \approx d/v$. We then multiply by the number of collisions per second $1/\tau_c$ and find for the relaxation time

$$1/T_1 = 2\,\gamma_1{}^2\,\gamma_2{}^2\,\hbar^2\,d^{-4}\,v^{-2}\,\tau_c{}^{-1} \tag{4. 41}$$

Substituting numerical values for He^3 at room temperature and atmospheric pressure, $v = 1.4 \times 10^5$ cm/sec., $\tau_c = 2 \times 10^{-10}$ sec, $d = 2 \times 10^{-8}$ cm, $\gamma_1 = \gamma_2 = 2.4 \times 10^4$, we find $T_1 = 10^6$ sec. In order to avoid saturation during the resonance measurements it is therefore necessary to admit oxygen gas. The magnetic moment of an O_2 molecule is about 10^3 times as large as of a He^3 atom.

Taking $\gamma_1 = 2.4 \times 10^4$, $\gamma_2 = 2.8 \times 10^7$, $d = 2.5 \times 10^{-8}$ cm, $\tau_c = 10^{-10}$ sec we find for the relaxation time of He^3 resonance, if the partial pressure of the oxygen is one atmosphere, $T_1 \approx 1$ sec. From (4. 41) and (4. 35) it follows that in this case the relaxation time is inversely proportional to the pressure. Strictly speaking we ought to add a term which is similar to (4. 41) to (4. 38) in the case of H_2. From the order of magnitudes, resulting from (4. 38) and (4. 41), we see that such a term in pure H_2 gas is completely negligible for pressures below 10^3 atmospheres. For O_2 pressures of 10^2 atmospheres, however, it is an important contribution. In general we can say that most gases, consisting of molecules, will behave like hydrogen and show the "anomalous" pressure-narrowing. The noble gases, consisting of atoms in an S-state, will behave like He^3 and have pressure broadening.

We shall now derive the relation between T_1 and T_2 for the case of He^3. At the same time we obtain an independent derivation of the saturation formula (2. 64). The He-nuclei can be considered as completely free most of the time, but during each collision there is a small chance for the nucleus to change its orientation. The probability $w = \frac{1}{2}T_1$ for such a transition is given by (4. 40). If a radio frequency field H_1 is switched on at $t = 0$, the free nuclei will oscillate between the upper and lower state according to Rabi's formula (2. 11), until the situation is interrupted by a thermal transition. We start out with the system of nuclei in thermal equilibrium. The situation can be described by the number of surplus nuclei, originally $+ n_o$ in the lower state, oscillating between $+ n_o$ and $-n_o$, while the collisions tend to restore the equilibrium value $+ n_o$. The probability that this is achieved in the time interval between t and $t + dt$ is given by $1/T_1 \exp(-t/T_1) \, dt$, as T_1 is the average time and the distribution of gas kinetic collisions in time is given by an exponential. The average energy dissipated from the spin system and absorbed during the collisions is

$$n_0 \, h \, \nu_0 \int_0^\infty w_{1/2, -1/2} \, \frac{1}{T_1} \, e^{-t/T_1} \, dt \qquad (4.42)$$

where $w_{1/2, -1/2}$ is the probability that the surplus nuclei are in the upper state at time t (2.11).

After the equilibrium has been restored, the process repeats itself. In our description we have artificially broken up the natural process into self repeating steps. In reality the individual nuclei each have a chance to make transitions both up and down, with a preference for the latter. The energy absorbed per second, which must be supplied by the radio frequency field, is obtained if we multiply (4.42) by $1/T_1$, the number of times that the process is repeated per second. The integration over t can be evaluated by partial integrations. The absorbed power P is given by

$$P = n_0 \, h \, \nu_0^3 \, \sin^2 \vartheta \, \frac{2 \pi^2 T_1}{1 + 4 \pi^2 T_1^2 (\nu^2 + \nu_0^2 - 2\nu \nu_0 \cos \vartheta)} \qquad (4.43)$$

Since always $H_1/H_o \ll 1$, we can put $\sin \vartheta \approx H_1/H_o$ and $\cos \vartheta \approx 1 - H_1^2/H_0^2$, $\gamma = 2\pi\nu_0/H_0$. Near resonance $\nu \approx \nu_0$ we then have

$$P = \frac{1}{4} \, n_0 \, h \, \nu_0 \, \gamma^2 \, H_1^2 \, \frac{2 T_1}{1 + T_1^2 (\omega - \omega_0)^2 + \gamma^2 H_1^2 T_1^2} \qquad (4.44)$$

which on comparison with (2.71) and (2.66) appears to be the B l o c h formula with $T_1 = T_2$.

It is interesting to apply the noise formula (3.21) to the case of He^3 and see what the minimum detectable amount is. It is not justified, however, to put in that formula $T_1 = T_2$, since the line width will always be determined by the inhomogeneity in the field. Using 10 atmospheres of O_2 we have $T_1 = 10^{-1}$ sec and we can take $T_2/T_1 \sim 10^{-2}$.

Substituting for q, λ and F each $\frac{1}{2}$ of their ideal values of unity and taking $Q = 10^2$, $\gamma = 2.4 \times 10^4$, $H_o = 10^4$, we find that 1 cc of He^3 gas at room temperature and atmospheric pressure would give a signal to noise ratio about 5, if the indication time of the meter is one second. In practice it would be very hard to find such a signal of such an extremely narrow line. One would have a better chance by searching for the moment in liquid He³ at 1° K.

Added in the proof:

Very recently A n d e r s o n (A 5) succeeded in measuring γ_{He^3} in a mixture of He³ and O_2, each at a partial pressure of 10 atmospheres.

4. 3.   *The relaxation time and line width in solids.*

4. 3. 1.   *Solids, to which the theory for liquids is applicable.*

In some solids there seems to be sufficient freedom of motion (S 5)

Figure 4. 8.

Values of the dielectric relaxation time τ defined by Debye, in ice at various temperatures. The points, indicated in the graph, are obtained from measurements of the anomalous dielectric dispersion in ice by Wintsch.

for the particles, that we can apply the same theory as in liquids. This state of affairs was already evident from the dielectric dispersion of the D e b y e type occurring in solids (D 2). The typical example is ice, of which we show the D e b y e time τ as a function of temperature in fig. 4.8.

The data are calculated from measurements by W i n t s c h (W 5). Of course, the molecules are not as free as in water; τ is about 10^6 times larger than in water. We expect then that the correlation time τ_c in the local field spectrum has increased by about the same factor, so that the relaxation time in ice will behave in the same way as in glycerin at low temperatures where $4\pi^2\nu_0{}^2\tau_c{}^2 \gg 1$. In fig. 4. 9 T_1 in ice between —2° C and —40° C is shown as a function of the Debye

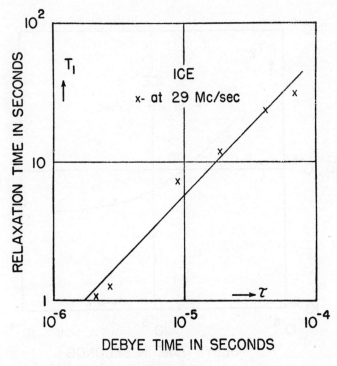

Figure 4. 9.

The relaxation time of the proton resonance in ice between — 2° C and — 40° C, plotted against the Debye time τ. The line drawn through the experimental points, makes an angle of 45° with the positive X-axis.

time, to which τ_c is proportional. The graph apparently confirms the ideas set forth in the beginning of this chapter. The straight line drawn through the points makes an angle of 45° with the x-axis. Unfortunately we were not able to investigate the resonance in ice at 4.8 Mc/sec, because the signal to noise ratio became too low in that case. We would

112

expect, of course, the relaxation time to be shorter, but having the same dependence on τ.

Measurements of the line width yield values of T_2, which are shown in fig. 4. 10. The drawn line is the theoretical curve computed from (4. 22). So here τ_c becomes so large that we approach the asymptotic value of the line width, which should be, according to the graph, about 16 oersted for a Gaussian. This is in good agreement with the value calculated from the crystal structure of ice (B 15), assuming that the

Figure 4. 10.

The line width of the proton resonance in ice between − 2° C and − 40° C. The theoretical curve (4. 22) for the quantity T_2, which is inversely proportional to the line width, is drawn through the experimental points.

nuclei are at rest. In ice a translational motion of the molecules in a viscous surrounding is apparently excluded. One might assume with D e b y e a hindered rotation of the H_2O molecules in the crystalline structure, although a more recent picture by Onsager suggests, that chains of lined up dipoles will reorient themselves at the positions, where

✢✢

there are misfits with other chains. Either picture will produce the required fluctuations in the local magnetic field and will only affect the proportionality constant between τ and τ_c. The best explanation for the fluctuations in the local field are perhaps the transitions between the two available positions for the proton in the O-H-O bond, as proposed by P a u l i n g (P 8). For comparison the results for alcohol, glycerin and ice at 29 Mc are shown together in fig. 4. 11. For glycerin we can

Figure 4. 11.

The relaxation time T_1 of the proton resonance in ethyl alcohol, glycerin and ice at 29 Mc/sec between $-40°$ C and $+60°$ C.

determine the ratio τ/τ_c from comparison of the experimental result of the minimum in the curve with formula (4. 25). We find $\tau_c = 2\,\tau$. Then we must have for alcohol $\tau_c = 0.2\,\tau$ and for ice $\tau_c = 0.8\,\tau$. These results are very satisfactory and must be considered as additional proof for our theory.

We now give a very brief account of what can be expected in other solids with some preliminary experimental results to confirm our view. Much more detailed investigations have to be carried out to refine the

✢✢✢

following global exposition. In hydrated paramagnetic salts like $CuSO_4$. 5 H_2O the field at the position of a proton will fluctuate, because the electron spins of the Cu^{++} ion change their quantisation with respect to H_o at the rate of the short electronic relaxation times ρ, to which we must put equal the correlation time τ_c. The proton resonance in $Cu\overline{S}O_4$. 5 H_2O and $CoSO_4$. 7 H_2O show line widths of only 12—14 oersted, while the instantaneous value of the internal fields in these paramagnetic salts is several hundred oersted. This can be explained by the short τ_c. The high intensity of local field, arising from the electronic moments, makes the relaxation time so short ($< 3 \times 10^{-4}$ sec), that we could not saturate the proton line.

In paraffin the relaxation time was found to be 0.01 sec. and the line width 4.5 oersted. These data are in agreement with the estimates of other investigators. In molten paraffin the line is narrow. Paraffin behaves again in a similar way as glycerin. In the solid state there still must be an appreciable opportunity for motion, either rotation or twisting or realignment, of the molecules. About the same as for solid paraffin holds for the F^{19} resonance in teflon. This carbon fluoride compound can be considered for our purpose as paraffin, in which the protons are replaced by F^{19} nuclei.

For the proton resonance in NH_4Cl a relaxation time of 0.12 sec. at $+ 20°$ C and 0.015 sec at $— 20°$ C was found. The line width at both temperatures was 4 oersted. These results can probably be explained by a hindered rotation of the NH_4 tetrahedron (S 5).

Very interesting experiments have been carried out by B i t t e r (B 2, A 1), who observed a sharp transition point in the line width of the proton resonance in solid CH_4, at the same temperature where there is known to be a transition point in the rotational degree of freedom of the molecule. The attention of the reader is also called to the measurements at very low temperatures by R o l l i n and collaborators (R 7). Possibly the rotation of the hydrogen molecule can be helpful in explaining the experimental results in solid ortho-hydrogen.

4. 3. 2. Ionic crystals; the influence of the lattice vibrations.

4. 3. 2. 1. The relaxation time.

We now take up the question of the relaxation time in those crystals, in which lattice vibrations are the only motion. For this case the theory of the relaxation time had been worked out by W a l l e r (W 1, H 2), who considered the interaction of the magnetic moments with the lattice vibrations. We shall show that our procedure, which gave the new results for liquids and gases, is essentially aequivalent to W a l l e r 's considerations, when it is applied to crystals.

For the lattice vibrations we shall adopt the same simplified picture, which D e b y e introduced in his theory of the specific heat of solids (S 5). According to this picture there is an isotropic distribution of lattice oscillators. In the volume V_c of the crystal there are $4 \pi \nu^2 V_c/c^3$ oscillators for one direction of polarisation in the frequency range ν, $\nu + d\nu$.

Here c denotes the velocity of propagation of elastic waves in the crystal, which is taken to be the same for longitudinal and transverse modes.

This formula is valid up to the frequency ν_m determined by the equation

$$\int_0^{\nu_m} 12 \pi \nu^2 V_c \, c^{-3} \, d\nu = 3 N \qquad (4.45)$$

For $\nu > \nu_m$ there are no lattice oscillators; (4.45) expresses that the total number of oscillators is equal to the degrees of freedom of the system of N atoms.

We first consider the contribution of one neighbour j to the Fourier spectrum of $\sum_j \sin \vartheta_{ij} \cos \vartheta_{ij} \, e^{i \varphi_{ij}} / r^3_{ij}$.

We take the z-axis in the direction of H_o. The radius vector $\vec{r}_{ij} = \vec{r}_i - \vec{r}_j$ connecting the equilibrium positions of the two nuclei makes an angle ϑ with the z-axis. The displacement $\vec{u}_i$ of the ith nucleus from its equilibrium position by the lattice vibrations is

$$\vec{u}_i = \sum_{\nu_k} \vec{A}_k \sin 2 \pi \nu_k (t - r_i/c + \varphi_k) \qquad (4.46)$$

The relative displacement of the ith and j^{th} nucleus for waves propagating in the direction of $\vec{r}_{ij}$

$$\triangle \vec{u}_{ij} = r_{ij} \sum_{\nu_k} \frac{2 \pi \nu_k}{c} \vec{A}_k \cos 2 \pi \nu_k (t - r_i/c + \varphi_k) \qquad (4.47)$$

since $\lambda_k = c/\nu_k \gg r_{ij}$. The variation in

$$F_1 = \sin \vartheta_{ij} \cos \vartheta_{ij} \, e^{i \varphi_{ij}}/r^3_{ij}$$

can be expressed by a Taylor series

❀❀❀

$$\triangle F_1 = \frac{\partial F_1}{\partial r} \triangle r + \frac{\partial F_1}{\partial \vartheta} \triangle \vartheta + \frac{\partial F_1}{\partial \varphi} \triangle \varphi + \frac{1}{2} \frac{\partial^2 F_1}{\partial r^2} (\triangle r)^2 + \dots . \quad (4.48)$$

We dropped the subscripts i and j. For longitudinally polarised waves we have only changes in r; for these $\triangle r = (\triangle u)$ long.

The direction of polarisation of one of the transverse modes is taken in the plane through $\vec{r}_{ij}$ and the z-direction. For this mode we have $r_{ij} \triangle \vartheta = (\triangle u)$ tr. I. For the second transverse mode we have $tg\triangle \varphi = (\triangle u)$ tr. II$/r \sin \vartheta$. If $\triangle u \ll r \sin \vartheta$, we may write $r \sin \vartheta \triangle \varphi = (\triangle u)$ tr. II. Only for very small ϑ this relation is not satisfied. For this last mode and very small values of ϑ the expansion (4.48) of F is not suitable.

To find the intensity J_1 (ν) of the spectrum of F_1, we have to determine the sum of the mean square deviations $(\triangle F_1)^2$ in each of the independent waves in the frequency interval ν, $\nu + d\nu$.

We can find an expression for the amplitude A_k of each wave by means of the aequipartition theorem. Each lattice vibrator has an energy $h\nu \Big/ \Big(e^{\frac{h\nu}{kT}} - 1 \Big)$ For small ν or large T this is equal to kT. Let M be the mass of the crystal, $\varrho = M/V_c$ the density. The æquipartition theorem can be written with (4.46) as

$$|A|^2 = \frac{h\nu}{2\pi^2 \nu^2 M \Big(e^{\frac{h\nu}{kT}} - 1 \Big)} \approx \frac{kT}{2\pi^2 \nu^2 M} \quad (4.49)$$

We use the last approximation for the three first order terms in (4.48). These terms can be treated independently, as they belong to different directions of polarisation. By squaring each of them and multiplying with the number of oscillators, we find with (4.47, 4.48, 4.49) for the intensity of the spectrum of the first orders terms

$$J_1(\nu) = \frac{4\pi \nu^2 V_c}{3 c^3} \frac{kT}{M} \frac{1}{r^6_{ij}} \Big[9 \sin^2 \vartheta_{ij} \cos^2 \vartheta_{ij} + \cos^2 2\vartheta_{ij} + \cos^2 \vartheta_{ij} \Big] \quad (4.50)$$

A factor $1/3$ is inserted, because the two directions of wave propagation perpendicular to $\vec{r}_{ij}$ do not contribute, as in those waves the two nuclei have the same phase.

Now we can sum (4.50) over all nuclei $j \neq i$. This is legitimate, although there are fixed phase relations between the deviations of the nuclei in one wave. For the quantisation of the various nuclei is independent, so that their fields aid or counteract at random. If we do not have a single crystal we can average over the angle ϑ, which yields a factor 2 for the expression between brackets in (4.50). The contribution of the Z nearest neighbours at a distance a will be the most important. Applying (2.53) we find for the relaxation time

$$1/T_1 = 4\pi\gamma^4\hbar^2 I(I+1) Z k T \nu_0^2/\varrho c^5 a^6 \qquad (4.51)$$

This result is essentially the same as W a l l e r's formula 51 (W 1, p. 386), derived for the transition probability of electronic spins with $I = \frac{1}{2}$. If we take $h\nu_0/kT \ll 1$, $\gamma = 2\,\mu/\hbar$ and multiply Waller's result by 2 to get $1/T_1$, we find that our numerical factor is $12\pi/5$ times larger. This difference could probably be explained by noting that W a l l e r used a more detailed picture for the lattice vibrations in a simple cubic lattice. He followed B o r n's representation of coupled harmonic oscillators. Furthermore W a l l e r quantised the lattice oscillators. To W a l l e r's result and our formula (4.51) a contribution of the processes in which two spins flop simultaneously should be added. It will appear to be much more important, however, to consider the influence of the second order terms in (4.48). On substitution of (4.47) into these terms we see that products of two harmonic functions are present and terms with frequency ν_0 in the expression of ΔF_1 occur as the sum or the difference of two frequencies ν_1 and ν_2. The whole spectrum of the lattice vibrations is important for the second order spectral intensity of F. Since the density of oscillators near the upper limit $\nu_{\rm m}$ is so much higher than at the frequency ν_0, it will turn out that the second order contributions are larger than the first order effects. We find by the same argument which led to (4.50) for the contribution of the first second order term in (4.48) to the spectral intensity

$${}''(\nu) = \frac{1}{18}\sin^2\vartheta_{ij}\cos^2\vartheta_{ij}\frac{3^2.4^2}{4 r^6_{ij} c^4}\int_0^{\nu_m}\int_{\substack{0 \\ \nu_1 \pm \nu_2 = \nu_0}}^{\nu_m}\frac{4\pi^2\nu_1^2 V_c h\nu_1}{Mc^3(e^{\frac{h\nu_1}{kT}}-1)}\cdot\frac{4\pi^2\nu_2^2 V_c h\nu_2}{Mc^3(e^{\frac{h\nu_1}{kT}}-1)}d\nu_1\,d\nu_2$$

and, since $\nu_0 \ll \nu_m$,

$$J_1''(\nu) \approx \frac{32\pi^2 h^2}{\varrho^2 c^{10}}\frac{\sin^2\vartheta_{ij}\cos^2\vartheta_{ij}}{r^6_{ij}}\int_0^{\nu_m}\frac{\nu'^6}{(e^{\frac{h\nu'}{kT}}-1)^2}d\nu' \qquad (4.52)$$

Since all frequencies up to ν_m are involved, we cannot make use of of the condition $x = h\,\nu'/k\,T \ll 1$, unless the temperature T is large compared to the Debye temperature $\Theta = h\,\nu_m/k$ of the crystal. The relaxation time, determined by this second order process, is by the same arguments which led to (4.51),

$$1/T_1 = \frac{8}{5}\,\gamma^4\,Z\,I\,(I+1)\,\frac{(k\,T)^7}{\varrho^2\,c^{10}\,a^6\,h^3}\int_0^{\Theta/T}\frac{x^6}{(e^x-1)^2}\,d\,x \qquad (4.53)$$

To (4.53) should be added the result of the other second order terms and the contribution of the double processes, in which two spins make a simultaneous transition. The numerical factor in (4.53) would become somewhat larger. But as it is, it is already $18\,\pi^2 \times 192/245$ larger than in W a l l e r's formula 56 (p. 388) for the quantised lattice oscillators. In the language of quantummechanics we can say that to (4.53) correspond transitions of the nuclear spin accompanied by the emission of a phonon and the absorption of another in the lattice. One could develop (4.48) to the third order terms, etc. It turns out that the contribution of the successive higher terms decreases as $k\,T\,\nu_m{}^3/\varrho\,c^5 \approx 10^{-2}$; so they can be neglected.

We see from (4.51) and (4.53) that the first order transition probability goes as T, the second order one as T^2 for $\Theta/T \approx 1$ but as T^7 for $\Theta/T \gg 1$. At room temperature the second order terms are more important. Substituting numerical values $\varrho = 2$, $c = 2 \times 10^5$, $\nu_0 = 3 \times 10^7$, $a = 2 \times 10^{-8}$, $Z = 6$, $\gamma = 3 \times 10^4$, $T = 300°$, $\Theta \ll T$ we find that (T_1) first order $\approx 10^{14}$ sec and (T_1) second order $\approx 10^3$ sec.

It was a surprise that, while W a l l e r 's theory predicted such long relaxation times for the nuclear magnetic resonance, the first experimental results gave much shorter times $(10^{-2}$ sec in paraffin). We have shown that in many solids the spectral intensity of the local field is caused by other motions than the lattice vibrations and that so many observed relaxation times could be explained. In ionic crystals like Ca F_2, however, one would expect W a l l e r 's theory to be applicable. Nevertheless the relaxation time for the F^{19} resonance in a single crystal of Ca F_2 appeared to be 8 sec. Relaxation times of the order of one second were also found in powdered Al F_3 and Na F, and by other authors in Li F. There are some indications that impurities and lattice defects play an important role in the relaxation process of these crystals (Compare the note at the end of this chapter).

✛✛

119

4. 3. 2. 2.   The line width.

The line width must be calculated from the components near zero frequency in the spectrum of $F_0 = \underset{ij}{\Sigma}(1 - 3\cos^2 \vartheta_{ij})/r^3_{ij}$. In the evaluation we can safely neglect the small and rapid lattice vibrations and assume that the nuclei are at rest. For this static problem the line width is given by (2. 36). It should be independent of the temperature, but vary with the orientation of the axes of a single crystal with respect to the direction of $\vec{H_o}$. Experiments (P 5) with a single crystal of Ca F_2 gave results for the line width in accordance with (2. 36) applied to the simple cubic lattice of F^{19} nuclei, the Ca ions having no magnetic moment. A detailed investigation of the line width in solids with special attention to the line shape was made by P a k e (P 1). In many compounds the same element can occur in more than one position in the unit cell of the crystal. When these positions are not aequivalent with respect to the internal magnetic field, one should distinguish more than one relaxation time and line width at the resonance of those nuclei. It is of no use, however, to discuss the situation in crystalline solids in detail, before more experimental material has become available.

Note added in the proof:

Recents experiments carried out in the Kamerlingh Onnes Laboratory of the University of Leiden confirm the hypothesis that the relaxation mechanism in ionic crystals is determined by paramagnetic impurities.

A theory, taking these into account, gives for T_1 a value of the order of a few seconds, if the crystal is contaminated with 0.0001 % iron. Furthermore this theory predicts that T_1 should be largely independent of the temperature of the lattice. These features are in striking contrast with W a l l e r's results for an ideal lattice and agree much better with the experimental data (comp. R 7).

A full account of these researches will be given elsewhere.

CHAPTER 5.

RELAXATION BY QUADRUPOLE COUPLING.

5. 1. *The influence of the quadrupole moment on the relaxation time and line width.*

If a nucleus has a spin $I > \frac{1}{2}$, the possibility of a spherically asymmetrical charge distribution over the nucleus exists. The value of the electric quadrupole momente eQ is defined in C a s i m i r's basic treatise (C 2) on the quantummechanics of the quadrupole moment as (compare however B 14)

$$e\,Q = \int (3\,z^2 - r^2)\,\varrho_{m_I = I}(\mathfrak{r})\,d\,\tau \qquad (5.1)$$

The integral is extended over the volume of the nucleus. The nuclear charge distribution is taken for the state with maximum z-component of the angular momentum $m_I = I$. The quantummechanical operator associated with the electric quadrupole moment consists of the components of a symmetrical tensor, the diagonal sum of which is zero. Since the group of rotations transforms these components in the same way as the Legendre polynomia of the second order, the components of the quadrupole moment can be shown to have the form

$$Q_{k\,l\,op.} = \frac{e\,Q}{I(2\,I - 1)} \left[\frac{3}{2}\,(I_k\,I_l + I_k\,I_l) - \delta_{k\,l}\,I^2 \right]_{op.} \qquad (5.2)$$

The subscripts $k, l,$ can each denote the x-, y- or z-component. Each of the components of the tensor is a matrix over the magnetic quantumnumber m_I. The matrix elements can easily be evaluated from (5.2) with the given form (1.1), (1.2) and (1.3) of the operators I_x, I_y and I_z. It is directly seen that $Q_{k,l}$ has only elements connecting states with $\Delta m = \pm 2, \pm 1$ or 0.

When a quadrupole moment is present, we have to add a term to the Hamiltonian

$$H_{Q\,op.} = \underset{\text{all nuclei}}{\Sigma} \left[-\frac{1}{6} \underset{k}{\Sigma} \underset{l}{\Sigma} Q_{k\,l} \times \frac{1}{2} \left(\frac{\partial_l}{\partial E_k} + \frac{\partial_k}{\partial E_l} \right) \right] \qquad (5.3)$$

The gradient of the components of the electric field $\vec{E}$, which occurs in this expression, is, of course, entirely due to the charge distribution in the sample. We do not apply an external inhomogeneous electric field. In heavy water e.g. the inhomogenous field at the position of a deuteron arises in the first place from the asymmetrical charge distribution of the other constituents in the same water molecule, but also from the electric dipoles of the neighbouring water molecules. We can now apply to the electric quadrupole perturbation (5. 3) the same considerations as we did in chapter 2 to the magnetic dipole interaction (2. 33). We note that because of the thermal motion of the molecules in the sample we again have a frequency spectrum of each of the components of $\text{grad}\,\vec{E}$. The correlation time τ_c for these components will be about the same as for the magnetic field, since for both τ_c is the time in which the position of the molecules with respect to H_o and one another has changed appreciably. The intensity of the spectrum of $\text{grad}\,\vec{E}$ at the Larmor frequency ν_0 of the nuclei is responsible for quadrupole transitions with $\Delta m = \pm 1$, the intensity of the spectrum at $2\,\nu_0$ for quadrupole transitions with $\Delta m = \pm 2$. These transitions shorten the relaxation time T_1. The components near the frequency zero in combination with the diagonal matrix elements of Q_{op} will broaden the resonance line. As an example of the terms we have to add to the formulae (2. 51) and (2. 53) for the relaxation time and line width, we write down the contribution to T_1 by the quadrupole moment of a nucleus with $I = 1$:

$$(1/T_1)_Q = \frac{1}{4}\frac{e^2 Q^2}{\hbar^2}\frac{\tau_c}{1 + 16\,\pi^2\nu^2\,\tau_c{}^2}\left\{\left(\frac{\partial E_x}{\partial x}\right)^2 + \left(\frac{\partial E_y}{\partial y}\right)^2 + \frac{1}{4}\left(\frac{\partial E_x}{\partial y} + \frac{\partial E_y}{\partial x}\right)^2\right\} +$$

$$+ \frac{1}{16}\frac{e^2 Q^2}{\hbar^2}\frac{\tau_c}{1 + 4\,\pi^2\,\nu^2\,\tau_c{}^2}\left\{\frac{1}{4}\left(\frac{\partial E_x}{\partial z} + \frac{\partial E_z}{\partial x}\right)^2 + \frac{1}{4}\left(\frac{\partial E_y}{\partial z} + \frac{\partial E_z}{\partial y}\right)^2\right\} \qquad (5.4)$$

5. 2. Experimental results for the resonance of H^2 and Li^7.

The influence of the quadrupole moment on the relaxation time has been observed for the resonance of the deuteron in water. Two samples were used. One contained 0.4 cc of a mixture of normal and heavy water, the other consisted of the same mixture with some $CuSO_4$ added. In both samples 51 % of the hydrogen nuclei were deuterons. The magnetic resonance of both protons and deuterons was observed at 4.8 Mc/sec and saturation curves were taken which are shown in fig. 5. 1. For comparison the proton resonance in normal water was also measured.

The relaxation time for the proton resonance in $H_2O + D_2O$ is about 1.4 times longer than in H_2O. This is due to the decreased intensity of the local magnetic field, since half of the protons are replaced by deuterons, of which the magnetic moment is about three times smaller.

The intensity of the local field at the position of a deuteron will be about the same as for a proton. It will be slightly higher because the percentages of H_2O, HDO and D_2O molecules in the liquid are such that the chance of a nearest neighbour of a deuteron to be a proton is

GENERATOR OUTPUT IN VOLTS

Figure 5. 1.

The saturation of the proton and deuteron resonance at 4.8 Mc/sec in light and heavy water.
a) Proton resonance in H_2O ;
b) Proton resonance in 49 % H_2O + 51 % D_2O ;
c) Proton resonance in 49 % H_2O + 51 % D_2O + $CuSO_4$:
d) Deuteron resonance in 49 % H_2O + 51 % D_2O ;
e) Deuteron resonance in 49 % H_2O + 51 % D_2O + $CuSO_4$.
The relaxation times calculated from the saturation curves can be found in the text.

larger than 49 %. The local field intensity, however, can certainly not be higher than in pure H_2O.

Suppose for the moment, that the deuteron would have no quadrupole moment. Then we expect, that the saturation of the d-resonance would occur at the same energy density of the applied radiofrequency field as the proton resonance, namely, when this density becomes comparable to that of the local field. We see, however, from fig. 5. 1 that the energy density, required for the saturation of the d-resonance, is 180 times higher. Taking into account that $\gamma^2_p/\gamma^2_d = 39$, we find that the relaxation time for the d-resonance in water is 0.5 sec, while it should be 90 sec, if no quadrupole moment were present. The explanation must be that the quadrupole moment of the deuteron is almost solely responsible for the observed short relaxation time. Substituting the values for T_1 and $Q = 2.73 \times 10^{-27}$ cm² in (5.4) we can estimate the value of $\operatorname{grad} \vec{E}$ in the liquid. It is the same as would be produced by one elementary charge at a distance of one Ångstrøm from the deuteron. This is a reasonable value for the inhomogeneity of the electric field in the molecule, surrounded by electric dipoles. So even small quadrupole moments can have a considerable effect.

Small concentrations of a paramagnetic salt will have no effect on the relaxation time, as the electric transitions remain more important at first than the magnetic ones. But the addition of a sufficient amount of $CuSO_4$ will increase the magnetic local field density so much that the relaxation time is then determined only by the magnetic transitions. The saturation of the p- and d-resonance then occurs at the same value of the applied field. The curves c and e show this situation. They should coincide exactly. The deviation of a factor 1.8 is probably due to a systematic error (cf. section 3.5). The inhomogeneity of the magnetic field for the p-resonance (at about 1100 oersted) is certainly different from that for the d-resonance (at about 7000 oersted).

One might ask why the influence of the quadrupole moment on the relaxation time of Li⁷ is not more pronounced. In the first place is the magnetic moment of Li⁷ rather large, making the relative influence of Q smaller.

Let us assume that the relaxation time of Li⁷ in an aqueous solution, which according to tabel IV is 1.75 sec, is for 50 % due to quadrupole interactions. The quadrupole moment Q of Li⁷ is not known experimentally. A very rough theoretical estimate by W e l l e s (W 4), built on the Hartree model, gives a value of -2.7×10^{-26} cm². On substitution of this value and $T_1 = 3.5$ sec in (5.4) we find that the gradient of the electric field is the same as produced by an elementary charge at least 3 Ångstrøm away. This distance seems to be too large, although one must expect that $\operatorname{grad} E$ is much smaller than in the case of the deuteron, since the Li⁺ ion is in a ¹S state and the neighbouring water dipoles will arrange themselves around the ion so as to give an approximately spherical charge distribution. It seems probable, that the quadrupole moment of Li⁷ is about five times smaller than the theoretical estimate, mentioned above.

The line width of the D² and Li⁷ resonance in the liquids used is determined by the inhomogeneity of the field H_o. The influence of the quadrupole moment could not be detected. P o u n d (P 9) recently has found broad resonance lines of the two Br isotopes in a solution of NaBr.

The width must be ascribed to the large quadrupole moments of these isotopes. P o u n d also discovered a fine structure of the Li⁷ resonance in a single crystal of $Li_2 SO_4$. The diagonal elements of (5.3), in which grad $\vec{E}$ can now be considered as a constant, give the first order perturbation of the four levels m_I which the Li⁷ nucleus can occupy in a magnetic field. If grad $\vec{E}$ is known from the crystal structure, the observed shift of the resonance frequencies enables one to determine the quadrupole moment Q.

5.3. The quadrupole interaction in free molecules.

The quadrupole interaction can be described more precisely, if we have to do with only one molecule. This is the case in molecular beam experiments (K 4) and in the application of the theory of the relaxation time to deuterium gas.

The grad $\vec{E}$ can then be written in terms of the angular momentum $\vec{J}_{op}$ of the molecule. By grouptheoretical arguments we have

$$\frac{1}{2}\left(\frac{\partial E_k}{\partial l} + \frac{\partial E_l}{\partial k}\right) = -\frac{e\,q}{J(2J-1)}\left[\frac{3}{2}\left(J_k J_l + J_l J_k\right) - \delta_{kl} J^2\right]_{op} \quad (5.5)$$

$$\text{with } e\,q = \int \frac{3\,z^2 - r^2}{r^5}\,\varrho_{m_J = J}(r)\,d\tau \quad (5.6)$$

The integration has to be extended over the charges of the molecule outside the nucleus under consideration, and for the state $m_J = J$.

The interaction term in the Hamiltonian can then be written as

$$H_{Q_{op}} = \frac{1}{2}\frac{e^2 q\,Q}{I(2I-1)\,J(2J-1)}\left[3\left(\vec{I}.\vec{J}\right)^2 + \frac{3}{2}\left(\vec{I}.\vec{J}\right) - \vec{I}^2\vec{J}^2\right]_{op}$$

$$(5.7)$$

We note that this operator has the same form as (4.36) and can be dealt with in the same way as described in chapter 4. For D_2 gas we must expect a shorter relaxation time than in H_2 gas, for the quadrupole interaction in the D_2 molecule is much larger than the magnetic interaction in H_2, as follows from the splitting of the lines of the resonance spectra obtained with the molecular beam method.

Finally we must mention a refinement of the theory given in chapter 2. When we consider the dipole-dipole interaction between two identical

protons in the same molecule, we should distinguish between ortho- and para-states, as we did for the hydrogen molecule. The magnetic interaction in a linear molecule will again assume the form (4.36). In a liquid J will probably not be constant of the motion which would make the problem involved. But J will usually be very high. The very light molecules like H_2 and D_2 are an exception in this respect. When J is large, we can introduce the classical approximation and replace J_z/J by $\cos \vartheta$ and $J_x + iJ_y/J$ by $\sin \vartheta \, e^{i \varphi}$ in the matrix elements (4.37). So we come back to formulae of the same form as (2.34) previously derived.

We do not touch the question how exchanges between nuclei in more complicated nuclei and between nuclei in neighbouring molecules should be taken into account. Under many circumstances — but not in H_2 and D_2 — the formulae (2.51) and (5.4), where all nuclei have been considered as distinguishable and the motion of the molecules is not quantised, will give a satisfactory description.

SUMMARY.

The exchange of energy between a system of nuclear spins immersed in a strong magnetic field, and the heat reservoir consisting of the other degrees of freedom (the "lattice") of the substance containing the magnetic nuclei, serves to bring the spin system into equilibrium at a finite temperature. In this condition the system can absorb energy from an applied radiofrequency field. With the absorption of energy however, the spin temperature tends to rise and the rate of absorption to decrease. Through this "saturation" effect, and in some cases by a more direct method, the *spin-lattice relaxation time* T_1 can be measured. The interaction *among* the magnetic nuclei, with which a characteristic time T_2' is associated, contributes to the width of the absorption line. Both interactions have been studied in a variety of substances, but with the emphasis on liquids containing hydrogen.

Magnetic resonance absorption is observed by means of a radiofrequency bridge; the magnetic field at the sample is modulated at a low frequency. A detailed analysis of the method by which T_1 is derived from saturation experiments is given. Special attention is paid ·to the influence of the inhomogeneity of the external magnetic field and to the limitation of the accuracy by noise. Relaxation times observed range from 10^{-4} to 10 seconds. In liquids T_1 ordinarily decreases with increasing viscosity, in some cases reaching a minimum value after which it increases with further increase in viscosity. The line width meanwhile increases monotonically from an extremely small value toward a value determined by the spin-spin interaction in the rigid lattice. The effect of paramagnetic ions in solution upon the proton relaxation time and line width has been investigated. The relaxation time and line width in ice have been measured at various temperatures.

The results can be explained by a theory which takes into account the effect of the thermal motion of the magnetic nuclei upon the spin-spin interaction. The local magnetic field produced at one nucleus by neighbouring magnetic nuclei, or even by electronic magnetic moments of paramagnetic ions, is spread out into a spectrum extending to frequencies of the order of $1/\tau_c$ where τ_c is a correlation time associated with the local Brownian motion and closely related to the characteristic time which occurs in D e b y e's theory of polar liquids. If the nuclear Larmor frequency ω is much less than $1/\tau_c$, the perturbations due to the local field nearly average out, $T_1 \sim 1/\tau_c$, and the width of the resonance line, in frequency, is about $1/T_1$. A similar situation is found in hydrogen gas where τ_c is the time between collisions. In very viscous liquids and in some solids where $\omega\,\tau_c > 1$, a quite different behavior is predicted, and observed.

Values of τ_c for ice, inferred from nuclear relaxation measurements, correlate well with dielectric dispersion data.

When the theory is applied to the motion embodied by the lattice vibrations of a crystal, it becomes identical to that of W a l l e r. The values for T_1 predicted by this theory are several orders of magnitude larger than those observed experimentally in ionic crystals.

The theory is also extended to the interaction of an electric quadrupole moment with an inhomogeneous internal electric field. The results are in good agreement with the observed relaxation time for the D^2-resonance in heavy water.

REFERENCES

A 1. N. L. Alpert, Phys. Rev. **72**, 637, 1947.

A 2. L. W. Alvarez and F. Bloch, Phys. Rev. **57**, 111, 1940.

A 3. H. L. Anderson and A. Novick, Phys. Rev. **71**, 878, 1947.

A 4. W. R. Arnold and A. Roberts, Phys. Rev. **71**, 878, 1947.

A 5. H. L. Anderson and A. Novick, Phys. Rev. (in press).

B 1. H. A. Bethe and R. F. Bacher, Rev. Mod. Phys. **8**, 82, 1936.

B 2. F. Bitter, N. L. Alpert, H. L. Poss, C. G. Lehr and S. T. Lin, Phys. Rev. **71**, 738, 1947.

B 3. P. Blacket and F. Champion, Proc. Roy. Soc. A **130**, 380, 1930.

B 4. F. Bloch, Phys. Rev. **70**, 460, 1946.

B 5. F. Bloch, A. C. Graves, M. Packard and R. W. Spence, Phys. Rev. **71**, 373, 1947; **71**, 551, 1947.

B 6. F. Bloch, W. W. Hansen and M. Packard, Phys. Rev. **69**, 127, 1946.

B 7. F. Bloch, W. W. Hansen and M. Packard, Phys. Rev. **70**, 474, 1946.

B 8. F. Bloch and I. I. Rabi, Rev. Mod. Phys. **17**, 237, 1946.

B 9. F. Bloch and A. Siegert, Phys. Rev. **57**, 522, 1940.

B 10. N. Bloembergen, R. V. Pound and E. M. Purcell, Phys. Rev. **71**, 466, 1947.

B 11. N. Bloembergen, E. M. Purcell and R. V. Pound, Nature **160**, 475, 1947.

B 12. L. J. F. Broer, *Beschouwingen en metingen over de paramagnetische relaxatie,* Thesis, Amsterdam 1945.

B 13. L. J. F. Broer, Physica **10**, 801, 1943.

B 14. J. Bardeen and C. H. Townes, Phys. Rev. **73**, 97, 1948.

B 15. J. O. Bernal and R. H. Fowler, J. Chem. Phys. **1**, 515, 1933.

C 1. H. B. G. Casimir, Physica **7**, 169, 1940.

C 2. H. B. G. Casimir, *On the interaction between atomic nuclei and electrons,* Archives du Musee Teyler, **8**, 202, 1936.

C 3. D. E. Coles and W. E. Good, Phys. Rev. **70**, 979, 1946.

C 4. E. H. Condon and G. H. Shortley, *Theory of atomic spectra,* Cambridge 1935.

C 5. C. H. Collie, J. B. Halsted and D. M. Ritson, Proc. Phys. Soc. **60**, 71, 1948.

C 6. R. L. Cummerow, D. Halliday and G. E. Moore, Phys. Rev. **72**, 1233, 1947.

D 1. B. P. Dailey, R. L. Kyhl, M. W. P. Strandberg, J. H. van Vleck and E. B. Wilson Jr., Phys. Rev. **70**, 984, 1946.

D 2. P. Debye, *Polar Molecules,* New York 1945, chapter 5.

D 3. R. Dicke, Rev. Sci. Inst. **17**, 268, 1946.

129

E 1. A. Einstein, Ann. Phys. **17**, 549, 1905; **19**, 371, 1906.

E 2. I. Estermann and O. Stern, Z. Phys. **85**, 17, 1933.

F 1. A. Farkas, *Light and Heavy Hydrogen*, Cambridge 1935.

F 2. R. Frisch and O. Stern, Z. Phys. **85**, 4, 1933.

G 1. Chr. Gehrtsen, Phys. Z. **38**, 833, 1937.

G 2. E. Gerjuoy and J. Schwinger Phys. Rev. **61**, 138, 1942.

G 3. C. J. Gorter, *Paramagnetic relaxation*, Amsterdam-New York, 1947.

G 4. C. J. Gorter, Physica **3**, 995, 1936.

G 5. C. J. Gorter and L. J. F. Broer, Physica **9**, 591, 1942.

G 6. C. J. Gorter and R. Kronig, Physica **3**, 1009, 1936.

G 7. P. Guttinger, Z. Phys. **73**, 169, 1931.

H 1. W. Heitler, *Quantumtheory of radiation*, Oxford 1936.

H 2. W. Heitler and E. Teller, Proc. Roy. Soc. **A 155**, 629, 1936.

J 1. L. C. Jackson, Proc. Phys. Soc. **50**, 707, 1938.

J 2. G. Joos, *Lehrbuch der Theoretischen Physik*, Leipzig 1939, page 205.

K 1. K. J. Keller, Thesis, Utrecht 1943.

K 2. J. M. B. Kellogg and S. Millman, Rev. Mod. Phys. **18**, 323, 1946.

K 3. J. M. B. Kellogg, I. I. Rabi, N. F. Ramsey and J. R. Zacharias, Phys. Rev. **56**, 728. 1939.

K 4. J. M. B. Kellogg, I. I. Rabi, N. F. Ramsey and J. R. Zacharias, Phys. Rev. **57**, 677, 1940.

K 5. H. Kopfermann, *Kernmomente*, Leipzig 1940.

K 6. H. A. Kramers, Hand und Jahrbuch der Chem. Physik I, Leipzig 1937.

K 7. H. A. Kramers, Atti Congr. Fis. Como, 545, 1927.

K 8. R. Kronig, Physica **5**, 65, 1938.

K 9. R. Kronig, J.O.S.A., **12**, 547, 1926.

K 10. R. Kronig and C. J. Bouwkamp, Physica **5**, 521, 1938.

K 11. R. King, H. R. Mimno and H. Wing, *Transmission lines, wave guides and antennae*, New York 1942.

K 12. P. Kusch, S. Millman and I. I. Rabi, Phys. Rev. **55**, 1176, 1939.

L 1. B. Lasarev and L. Shubnikow, Phys. Z. Sowjetunion, **11**, 445, 1937.

M 1. E. Majorana, Nuovo Cimento, **9**, 43, 1932.

M 2. J. M. W. Milatz and N. Bloembergen, Physica **11**, 449, 1945.

M 3. S. Millman, Phys. Rev. **55**, 628, 1939.

M 4. N. F. Mott, Proc. Roy. Soc. **A 126**, 259, 1930.

P 1. G. E. Pake, J. Chem. Phys. (in press).

P 2. W. Pauli, Naturwissenschaften **12**, 741, 1924.

P 3. R. V. Pound, E. M. Purcell and H. C. Torrey, Phys. Rev. **69**, 680, 1946.

P 4. E. M. Purcell, Phys. Rev. **69**, 681, 1946.

P 5. E. M. Purcell, N. Bloembergen and R. V. Pound, Phys. Rev. **70**, 988, 1946.

P 6. E. M. Purcell, R. V. Pound and N. Bloembergen, Phys. Rev. **70**, 986, 1946.

P 7. E. M. Purcell, H. C. Torrey and R. V. Pound, Phys. Rev. **69**, 37, 1946.

P 8. L. Pauling, *The Nature of the Chemical Bond*, p. 302 ff, Cornell 1940.

P 9. R. V. Pound, Phys. Rev. **72**, 1273, 1947.

R 1. I. I. Rabi, Phys. Rev. **51**, 652, 1937.

R 2. I. I. Rabi, S. Millman, P. Kusch and J. R. Zacharias, Phys. Rev. **55**, 526, 1939.

R 3. W. R a r i t a and J. S c h w i n g e r, Phys. Rev. **59**, 436 and 556, 1941.

R 4. S. O. R i c e, Bell Tel. J. **23**, 282, 1944; **25**, 46, 1945.

R 5. B. V. R o l l i n, Nature **158**, 669, 1946.

R 6. B. V. R o l l i n and J. H a t t o n, Nature **159**, 201, 1947.

R 7. B. V. R o l l i n, J. H a t t o n, A. H. C o o k e and R. J. B e n z i e, Nature **160**, 436, 1947.

R 8. M. E. R o s e, Phys. Rev. **53**, 715, 1938.

S 1. R. S a c h s, Phys. Rev. **71**, 457, 1947.

S 2. H. S c h ü l e r and T h. S c h m i d t, Z. Phys. **94**, 457, 1935.

S 3. J. S c h w i n g e r, Phys. Rev. **51**, 648, 1937.

S 4. J. S c h w i n g e r, Phys. Rev. **55**, 235, 1939.

S 5. F. S e i t z, *Modern Theory of Solids,* New York 1940.

T 1. C. H. T o w n e s, A. N. H o l d e n, J. B a r d e e n and F. R. M e r r i t t, Phys. Rev. **71**, 644, 1947.

V 0. G. A. V a l l e y 'and H. W a l l m a n, Radiation Laboratory Series, Vol. 18, Mc Graw-Hill.

V 1. J. H. v a n V l e c k, *Theory of electric and magnetic susceptibilities,* Oxford 1932.

V 2. J. H. v a n V l e c k, Phys. Rev. **55**, 924. 1939.

V 3. J. H. v a ı V l e c k, Phys. Rev. (in press).

W 1. I. W a l l e r, Z. Phys. **79**, 370, 1932.

W 2. M i n g C h e n W a n g and G. E. U h l e n b e c k, Rev. Mod. Phys. **17**, 323, 1945.

W 3. V. W e i s k o p f and E. W i g n e r, Z. Phys. **63**, 54, 1930; **65**, 18, 1930.

W 4. S. H. W e l l e s, Phys. Rev. **62**, 197, 1942.

W 5. H. W i n t s c h, Helvetica Phys. Acta **5**, 126, 1932.

Z 1. E. Z a v o i s k y, J. Phys. U.S.S.R **9**, 211, 1945; ibid. 245 and 447.

ON THE INTERACTION
OF NUCLEAR SPINS
IN A CRYSTALLINE LATTICE

ON THE INTERACTION OF NUCLEAR SPINS
IN A CRYSTALLINE LATTICE

by N. BLOEMBERGEN *)

Communication No. 277a from the Kamerlingh Onnes Laboratorium, at Leiden

Summary

The exchange of energy between a system of nuclear spins, immersed in a strong magnetic field H_0, and the lattice vibrations of insulating crystals has been investigated experimentally by the method of nuclear magnetic resonance absorption. The resonance in calciumfluoride, some hydrated sulphates and some alkalihalides, has been observed between $300°K$ and $1°K$, at 30.5 and 9.5 Mc/sec. The measured spin-lattice relaxation times T_1 range from 10^{-3} to 10^4 sec, and disagree violently — in many cases by more than a factor 10^6 — with Waller's theory of paramagnetic relaxation. It is shown that the relaxation time T_1 is determined by paramagnetic impurities occurring in the lattice. An order of magnitude theory is developed taking these impurities into account. The quanta absorbed by the system of nuclear spins from the external radiofrequency field diffuse toward the impurities. The energy is then transferred to the lattice vibrations via the fluctuating magnetic field from the impurity. The first process depends on the concentration of the impurities, the second on H_0 and on the relaxation time ϱ of the impurity. The experimental data receive at least qualitative explanation in terms of these quantities.

In some cases a direct heat contact between the system of nuclear spins and the system of impurity spins proves to be important. Then T_1 is independent of the lattice temperature.

1. *Introduction*. The exchange of energy between a system of nuclear spins immersed in a strong magnetic field, H_0, and the other degrees of freedom (the "lattice") of the substance containing the magnetic nuclei has been investigated theoretically and experimentally by P u r c e l l, P o u n d and the present author. Their paper [1] [2], henceforth referred to as l.c., describes the situation, broadly speaking, in the following manner.

---

*) Present address: Society of Fellows, Harvard University.

Each spin of a system of N non-interacting spins in the field H_0 has $2I + 1$ energy levels spaced by an amount $\gamma \hbar H_0$, where γ is the magnetogyric ratio. A weak radiofrequency field $H_1 \exp i\omega_0 t$, satisfying the conditions $H_1 \perp H_0$ and $\omega_0 = 2\pi v_0 = \gamma H_0$, will induce transitions between these levels. If equilibrium at some finite temperature would exist, the states with lower energy would be more densely populated according to a Boltzmann distribution. Then more transitions would occur from a lower to a higher level than vice versa, resulting in a net absorption of energy by the nuclear spins from the radiofrequency field.

A system of non-interacting spins, however, would never come to thermal equilibrium. It is shown in l.c., how the dipole-dipole interaction between the magnetic nuclei, in combination with the thermal variation of the space coordinates of the nuclei, provides a heat contact between the spins and the other degrees of freedom. This heat contact may be measured by a characteristic time, T_1. This spin-lattice relaxation time indicates how long one must wait after the application of the constant field H_0 for the establishment of thermal equilibrium. The application of the oscillating field tends to upset this equilibrium, since energy is supplied to the spins, which energy must be dissipated through the relaxation process mentioned above. The temperature of the spin system will rise to a new equilibrium value, where the effect of the externally applied radiation field is counter-balanced by that of the internal or local magnetic field arising from the nuclear dipoles in the substance. The intensity of this latter field at the resonance frequency of the nuclei tends to restore thermal equilibrium.

Apart from its importance for the energy dissipation, the local field also determines the shape of the nuclear magnetic resonance absorption line. The relaxation theory proposed in l.c. gave results which agree with experiments on liquids, gases and a certain class of solids, examples of which are ice, paraffin, ammoniumhalides. Experimental results in metals [7] [29] agree with Heitler's theory [3]. In all these substances other types of thermal motion occur than just the lattice vibrations. When the theory was applied to an ionic insulating crystal like CaF_2, for which it is reasonable to assume that the lattice vibrations are the only type of thermal motion, there is a disagreement between the theoretical and experimental value of T_1 of more than a factor 10^6. In fact the theory of l.c. then merely

　　　　　N. BLOEMBERGEN

duplicates the results which had already been obtained by W a l-
l e r [4]) in 1932 and discussed by H e i t l e r and T e l l e r [3]) in
1936. The theoretical values for T_1 in a crystal of CaF_2, as derived
from Waller's formulae, are plotted in fig. 1 as a function of the
absolute temperature. In early experiments $T_1 = 8$ sec was found in

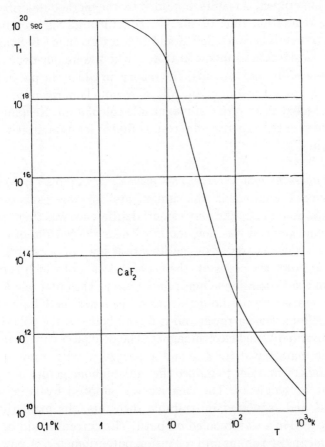

Fig. 1. The relaxation time of F^{19} resonance in a crystal of CaF_2 in a field of
7000 oersted, calculated with Waller's theory.

a single crystal of CaF_2 at room temperature in contrast to the
astronomical figure along the ordinate of fig. 1. It was suggested
that paramagnetic impurities might play a predominant role in the
relaxation process [2]) [5]). Even more striking contradiction with theory
was found by R o l l i n [6]), who was the first to investigate nuclear
magnetic resonance at low temperatures. He measured a value T_1 of

a few seconds in LiF at 1.5°K. Independently that author also arrived at the conclusion [7]) that impurities are most important, in a note which was published during the course of this work. It seemed worth while to undertake a systematic investigation about the rôle of impurities in crystalline lattices in a large interval of temperatures.

The experimental results, obtained by the method described in § 2 for the relaxation time of the H^1, F^{19}, Li^7 and Na^{23} resonance in various crystals between 300°K and 1 °K are given in § 3. Some theoretical considerations follow in §§ 4–6, which were developed during the course of the experiments. The theory, in which the paramagnetic impurities play a predominant rôle, does not claim rigour and should be considered as an order of magnitude calculation. Keeping this in mind most of the experimental results find at least qualitative explanation in § 7.

2. *Apparatus and experimental method. a.* A p p a r a t u s. The experimental equipment was similar, and in some parts identical, with that used in l.c. The only essential difference was that the small radiofrequency coil was now mounted near the bottom of a Dewar vessel in order to carry out experiments at low temperatures.

Fig. 2 shows the cryostat, the general design of which is conventional in the Kamerlingh Onnes Laboratory. The outer one E of two Dewar vessels contains liquid nitrogen, the inner one F liquid hydrogen or helium. The narrower end is placed between the poles O of an Oerlikon watercooled electromagnet. The pole pieces are 5 cm apart, 14 cm in diameter at the gap and are supplied with a raised rim at the periphery in order to reduce the radial inhomogenity of the field inherent to geometry. The current was supplied by large storage batteries and regulated by suitable rheostats, the main rheostats being placed in a watercooled oil bath. The current could be monired by means of a shunt and a Tinsley potentiometer. A power of 1 kilowatt was required to obtain a field of 7000 oersted. The homogeneity of the field over the region of the sample was better than 0.5 oersted, and the variations in time, due to instability of the current source, were sufficiently small for the investigation of the wide resonance lines. For we may state at once that in all solids which we investigated, the line width was larger than 4 oersted, so that we were always dealing with lines of natural width. The field could be modulated at 25 c.p.s. by means of two auxiliary coils around the pole pieces, having 100 turns each. An a.c. current of 1 A. provided a 20 oersted peak to peak modulation. The 25 c.p.s. signal was derived from a suitably filtered multivibrator, locked to the frequen-

Fig. 2a and 2b. The cryostat containing the coil, in which the nuclear magnetic resonance takes place. The description is given in the text.

cy of the mains. The necessary power was supplied by two balanced 6 L 6 tubes.

The coil H consisted of 12 turns of 1 mm bare copper wire, wound around a glass cylinder of 9 mm outside and 8 mm inside diameter. The coil was soldered to the inner and outer conductor N and L, of a coaxial line leading through the cap of the cryostat. Both conductors consisted of thin walled german silver tubing, spaced by polystyrene spacers M, and terminated into a standard u.h.f. connector K.

In the glass cylinder, which was cemented on to the coaxial line, another thinwalled tube I containing the samples could be moved by raising, lowering or turning (the latter was important for the work on single crystals) the wire C leading through the packing A. Four samples separated by glass wool P could be brought into the coil without opening the cryostat. This feature is very important in order to avoid time delay in low temperature work. A disadvantage was the smaller filling factor of the coil. The coil was separated from the liquid in the cryostat by a brass envelope J, which could be opened at the soft-soldered joint G. The room inside the envelope was evacuated via the pump lead B and filled with He-gas of a few cm pressure at room temperature to ensure thermal contact with the bath. By this arrangement we eliminated the change in stray capacity of the coil by gas bubbles and a spurious proton signal of liquid or gaseous hydrogen, when the cryostat was filled with it. The bath temperature could be determined from the vapour pressure over the liquified gas. Data were taken at 77°K (boiling point of nitrogen). 20.3°K (boiling point of hydrogen), 14°K, 4.2°K (boling point of helium), 2.1°K and 1.2°K. Data at room temperature were taken in another coil with a somewhat higher Q and better filling factor.

In the early experiments a spurious proton signal arose from the silk insulation and cement, fixing the coil to the glass coil form. Although the total number of protons in the insulating material was much smaller than in the investigated salts, their influence was greatly enhanced by a shorter relaxation time, and narrower resonance line. So we finally used the coil of bare wire described above.

The radiofrequency circuit is shown in the block diagram of fig. 3. For details the reader is referred to l.c. The only modification is that the coil in the cryostat is connected to its tuning condenser by an extra half wave length of coaxial line. It was found that ceramic condensers exhibit irreversible changes when cooled to low

✦✦

temperatures. In our arrangement all condensers were at room temperature and the bridge could easily be balanced to 50 d.b. The bridge elements could be replaced in a few minutes in changing from one frequency to the other. The loaded Q of the circuit was about 80 at 30.5 Mc/sec and 50 a 9.5 Mc/sdc at all temperatures. The oscillator was a General Radio 805-C signal generator. The maximum output of 2 V into 75 Ω was not sufficient to measure relaxation times shorter than $5 \cdot 10^{-3}$ sec with the wide lines ($\approx$ 15 oersted) *), occurring in the solids. We were, however, able to saturate most samples †).

Fig. 3. Block diagram of the electric circuit.
A. Signal generator. — B. Radiofrequency bridge. — C. Communications receiver. — D. Phase sensitive 25 c.p.s. mixer. — E. 25 c.p.s. oscillator. — F. Phase shifter and power amplifier. — G. Cathode ray oscillograph. — H. Modulation coils. — L. Nuclear magnetic resonance coil in magnet gap.

The receiver was a Hallicrafters R 45/ARR-7, preceded at 30.5 Mc/sec by a preamplifier taken from a RT 39A/APG5 radar set. The noise figure was then improved by about 8 db.

Circuit diagrams for the audio oscillator and fase mixer have been given elsewhere [2]).

---

*) In this paper $\approx$ denotes "of the order of", while $\sim$ is used for "proportional to".
†) An additional r.f. power amplifier is now under construction.

b) M e t h o d. Two methods have been described in l.c. to measure the relaxation time T_1 and both have been applied in the present investigation. It may be said at once, that the accuracy is not better than 10% and in unfavorable cases may rise to 30%. But this is no serious limitation, as we shall see that we are primarily interested in variations of T_1 of several orders of magnitude.

Fig. 4. The re-establishment of temperature equilibrium of the system of F^{19} spins in CaF_2 at 2.1°K after saturation. D_{max} is the peak absorption. The drawn curve is the exponential function $13.5(1 - e^{t/7})$.

The most direct determination of T_1 is to follow the cooling off of the nuclear spin system, after it has been heated by a strong r.f. signal. The subsequent absorption in a very weak r.f. field is inversely proportional to the spin temperature T_S and is made visible on the screen of a cathode ray tube, while the magnetic field is modulated with an amplitude larger than the line width. For $T_1 > 5$ sec the growth of the absorption curve can easily be followed visually as a function of the time. Figure 4 gives a plot of the maximum absorption in a single crystal of CaF_2 at 2.1°K as a function of time after the sudden reduction of r.f. power at $t = 0$. The drawn curve is the function 13.5 $\{1 - \exp(-t/7)\}$, from which we infer that $T_1 = 7$ minutes in this case.

The lines of the investigated salts had natural widths between 4 and 20 oersted. The maximum absorption is inversely proportional to the line width and is for the 14 oersted wide proton line in $KAl(SO_4)_2 \cdot 12H_2O$ at 2°K about as large as for a 0.1 oersted wide proton line in water at 300°K.

Because of noise the direct observation on the oscilloscope was only possible at temperatures below 20°K. At these low temperatures relaxation times as long as half an hour were observed in some samples. Care should be taken that the r.f. field in the coil has a correspondingly low intensity in measuring the relaxation time. The probability for induced transitions should be small compared to $1/T_1$

When very long relaxation times were measured, each proton made less than one transition per hour in the external r.f. field, which then had an amplitude of about $2 . 10^{-4}$ oersted. In addition this field was only turned on once every two or three minutes during ten seconds in taking data.

When the signal to noise ratio is insufficient for observation on the oscilloscope, the maximum deflection on the output meter of the audio phase mixer may be measured as a function of time. The 25 c.p.s. modulation is then of course reduced to a fraction of the line width. Instead of diminishing the output of the oscillator P a k e [30]) shifts the magnetic field off resonance, when no data are taken.

For values of $T_1 < 200$ sec the saturation curve method was used. This method gives only relative values for T_1, but as values of T_1 between 5 and 200 sec were taken by both methods, absolute calibration points were obtained.

The maximum deflection of the meter, D_{ex}, is measured in the steady·state as a function of the amplitude H_1 of the r.f. field. When saturation sets in, that is when H_1 is so large that the equilibrium temperature of the nuclear spin system starts to rise appreciably, the proportionality constant between the maximum absorption and H_1^2 decreases. Let $g(\nu)$ be the natural shape of the absorption line. Define the function $S(\nu) = \{1 + \frac{1}{2}\gamma^2 H_1^2 T_1 g(\nu)\}^{-1}$ and denote the modulation frequency by ν_m. Then we have (compare l.c.)

Case 1 $2\pi \nu_m T_1 \ll 1$ $D(\nu) \sim \dfrac{\partial}{\partial \nu} g(\nu) S(\nu)$ (1)

Case 2 $2\pi \nu_{\mathrm{m}} T_1 \gg 1$ $D(\nu) \sim S(\nu) \dfrac{\partial}{\partial \nu} g(\nu)$ (2)

From these relations the extreme values of $D(\nu)$ may be found for any line shape. In fig. 7 of l.c. the results are given for

$$g(\nu) = \frac{2T_2}{1 + 4\pi^2 (\nu - \nu_0)^2 T_2^2},$$

appropriate for a damped oscillator.

It should be emphasized, that in many substances we have investigated, the line shape is completely different. The function $g(\nu)$ e.g. for protons in powder samples of hydrated salts like $KAl(SO_4)_2$. $.12H_2O$ and $ZnSO_4.7H_2O$ exhibits two flat maxima, about 14 oersted apart. This was first found by P a k e [8]). In CaF_2 $g(\nu)$ is more

Fig. 5. Saturation curves for the proton resonance at 77°K in $KAl(SO_4)_2.12H_2O$ with different amounts of Cr^{+++} impurity.

similar to a Gaussian distribution. When we compare lines with the same shape we may say that D_{ex} is a function of the saturation parameter $s = \gamma^2 H_1^2 T_1 T_2$, and when D_{ex} is plotted against the output voltage of the signal generator — to which H_1 is proportional — on semi-logarithmic paper, we should obtain a series of parallel curves, of which fig. 5 gives an example.

From the horizontal distance of these curves we can determine the ratio $\gamma^2 T_1 T_2$. For most substances it was possible to make a direct determination of T_1 at low temperatures with the first method and since the line shape is independent of the temperature for the crystals, values of T_1 can be derived immediately from the horizontal distance of the curves. This is only true when $\omega_{\mathrm{m}} T_1 \gg 1$ remains valid at the higher temperatures, as was mostly the case. When $T_1 \approx 0.01$ sec or less, we approach case 1, and a correction must be applied, which may be calculated from (1) and (2). For a damped oscillator curve the correction factor is about 0.5. When lines of different shapes are compared the necessary corrections could also be calculated from (1) and (2), if the precision of the data warrants and if the modulation amplitude is very small compared to the width. Usually this correction will not be important and saturation will occur for the same value of the parameter $\gamma^2 H_1^2 T_1 T_2$. Then only the knowledge of γ and T_2 is necessary to infer the relative value of T_1 from the saturation curves. The value of T_2 could be obtained from direct measurement of the line width. But for all substances con sidered in this paper it is safe to calculate T_2 from a well established theoretical formula[9]) derived for a rigid lattice (l.c. equation 25):

$$(1/T_2)^2 = \gamma_i^2 \, \hbar^2 \, \{\Sigma_j \tfrac{3}{4} \gamma_j^2 \, I_j \, (I_j + 1) \, (1 - 3 \cos^2 \vartheta_{ij})^2 \, r_{ij}^{-6} +$$

$$+ \Sigma_k \tfrac{1}{3} \gamma_k^2 \, I_k \, (I_k + 1) \, (1 - 3 \cos^2 \vartheta_{ik})^2 \, r_{ik}^{-6} \}. \tag{3}$$

Here r_{ij} is the radius vector between nuclei i and j, ϑ_{ij} is its angle with the direction of H_0.

The sum over j contains nuclei, identical with i; the sum over k only non-identical nuclei. The average value $\overline{(1 - 3 \cos^2 \vartheta)^2} = {}^4/_5$ may be taken for a powder. In figure 6 the saturation curves for the F^{19} and Na^{23} resonance in NaF powder at 2.1°K are represented. The values of γ and T_2 being known for the two nuclei, we obtain $(T_1)_{Na} : (T_1)_F = 11.5$. This is in good agreement with the values $(T_1)_{Na} = 180$ sec and $(T_1)_F = 15$ sec, obtained from direct observation on the oscilloscope.

Finally we give in figure 7 an example of the saturation of the F^{19} resonance in a single crystal of CaF_2. Curve II was taken, when the 1, 1, 1 axis was parallel·to the external field H_0, curve I when the 1, 0, 0 axis was parallel to H_0. One finds for the ratio of the products $T_1 T_2$ in the two cases 2.4 ± 0.3, while it is known [9]) from P a k e 's measurements and from the theoretical formula (3) that the ratio of the values of T_2 is 2.3.

So we may conclude that T_1 is the same for the two orientations.

3. *Experimental results.* a) C a l c i u m   f l u o r i d e. We investigated four different specimens of this substance:

I. a single crystal, cut from a clear, almost colourless natural spe-

Fig. 6 (below) and Fig. 7 (above).
Saturation curves for Na^{23} and F^{19} in NaF powder at 2.1°K.
Saturation curves for F^{19} in a single crystal of CaF_2.
Curve I was taken, when H_0 was parallel to the 1, 0, 0 axis, curve II
when H_0 was parallel to the 1, 1, 1 axis.

cimen. The shape was cylindrical, 8 mm diameter and 20 mm height.
The 1, 1, 0 direction was parallel to the axis.

III. a single crystal, cut from another almost colourless natural
specimen *). The dimensions of the cylinder were about the same as
for crystal I.

II. a powder sample, made from the same natural specimen,
from which crystal II was cut.

IV. a powder sample, obtained commercially (Kahlbaum purissi-
mus).

A chemical analysis revealed that IV contained 0.014% of iron
(in weight), and I 0.001% iron **).

*) We appreciate the courtesy of Professor E s c h e r of the Mineralogy Department
for kindly supplying us with these two crystals.

**) This analysis and many others mentioned in this paper were carried out by the staff
of the Laboratory of Anorganic Chemistry in Leiden. We wish to express our indebtedness
to Professor V a n A r k e l for his precious cooperation.

Figure 8 gives the experimental results for the relaxation time in these specimen, while the F^{19} resonance was observed at 30.5 Mc/sec and 9.5 Mc/sec. The curves for II and III coincide. It was, moreover,

Fig. 8. The relaxation time T_1 in various samples of CaF_2 as a function of temperature. The drawn curves are for data taken at 30.5 Mc/sec, the dotted ones for 9.5 Mc/sec.

found that T_1 is independent of the orientation of the single crysstal at all temperatures. It is seen that IV which contains the largest iron impurity has the shortest relaxation times, while the two single crystals differ by a factor 5 in the value of T_1 at temperatures above 20°K. In this region T_1 is independent of the temperature while it rises approximately as T^{-2} below 14°K. In sample IV the relaxation time goes about as T^{-1} over the whole temperature range. At 9.5 Mc/sec the relaxation times are generally shorter by a factor 2 or 3 except for the single crystal II at 20°K, where T_1 does not seem to change appreciably with the frequency. Unfortunately the measurements at 9.5 Mc/sec could not be extended to higher temperatures because of the unfavorable signal to noise ratio.

The discussion of the results will be postponed until § 7. But it is seen at once that impurities play a predominant rôle in the nuclear relaxation process. In fact T_1 is not a characteristic of a chemical crystalline substance, but of its paramagnetic impurities. Comparison of figures 1 and 8 shows clearly that Waller's theory is inadequate not only in order of magnitude, but also in its predicted dependence upon temperature.

In order to compare experimental results and theory it is necessary to have samples, in which the amount and the nature of the impurity is known.

b) Potassium-aluminium alum. We therefore investigated the proton resonance in this hydrated salt, in which we could replace a known percentage of the Al-ions by Cr-ions. The powdered samples were obtained from clear crystals, out of saturated solutions, in which Al- and Cr-alum were mixed in various proportions. The crystals were analysed afterwards and it was found, that the Cr-content differed by about a factor 2 from that in the solution, and the crystals from each solution had the same Cr-constant.

The results are collected in table I.

TABLE I

Sample	Cr-content percentage weight	Number of atoms Cr : Al
I	0%	trace of iron
II	0.00073%	1 : 28000
III	0.0064 %	1 : 3200
IV	0.054 %	1 : 380
V	0.70 %	1 : 29

The values for the relaxation time of the resonance at 30.5 Mc/sec and at 9.5 Mc/sec are given in figures 9 and 10. The data of figure 9

N. BLOEMBERGEN

are replotted in figure 11 as a function of the concentration and in
figure 12 as a function of the spin-lattice relaxation time ϱ of the

Fig. 9. The relaxation time T_1 for the proton
resonance at 30.5 Mc/sec in $KAl(SO_4)_2 . 12H_2O$,
containing different amounts of Cr^{+++}, as a
function of temperature.

Fig. 10. The relaxation time T_1 for
the proton resonance at 9.5 Mc sec
in $KAl(SO_4)_2 . 12H_2O$, containing
different amounts of Cr^{+++}, as a
function of temperature.

impurity. The reasons for this way of plotting will become clear
later on.

Fig. 11. The relaxation time T_1 for the proton resonance at 30.5 Mc/sec in
$KAL(SO_4)_2 . 12H_2O$ as a function of the Cr-concentration.

It is seen that the values in the so-called "pure" Al-alum fit the
extrapolated experimental curves, if an impurity of about two parts

✈✈✈

in a million of iron is assumed. (It will be made clear later that a Cr^{+++} or Fe^{+++} impurity behave in approximately the same way).

Such a small concentration of iron may be expected in most chemical reagents which have not been especially prepared. The dependence of T_1 on the number of impurities per cc N is given by $N^{-0.8}$ at room temperature and $T_1 \sim N^{-1.2}$ at 20°K. Figure 12 shows that approximately $T_1 \sim \varrho^{0.7}$ in very diluted substances and $T_1 \sim \varrho^{0.5}$ in sample IV. In sample I and II T_1 is certainly larger than 2000 sec at 2.1°K. In sample IV T_1 seems to reach an asymptotic

Fig. 12. The relaxation time T_1 for the proton resonance at 30.5 Mc/sec in $KAL(SO_4)_2 . 12H_2O$ as a function of the spin lattice relaxation time ϱ of the Cr-impurities.

value T_1'' of 20 sec at low temperatures, while the slope of III also seems to decrease at 1.1°K. Sample V could not be saturated with the available power of the generator. The relaxation time is shorter than 10^{-2} sec over the whole range. It is believed that it is not very much shorter than 10^{-2} sec as always an indication for the onset of saturation was found.

At 9.5 Mc/sec the relaxation time is shorter, except in specimen V, and the constant value T_1'' at low temperatures in specimen III and IV is more pronounced.

The line width in samples I to IV was about 14 oersted and the shape seemed to be in agreement with Pake's accurate measure-

Fig. 13. The relaxation time T_1 for the proton resonance at 30.5 Mc/sec in $CsAl(SO_4)_2.12H_2O$ with Ti^{+++} impurity as a function of temperature.

ments. In V the line was broadened to about 20 oersted by the internal fields of Cr^{+++} impurities. In pure $KCr(SO_4)_2.12H_2O$ a vestige of a very broad line, about 100 oersted wide, was observed at 14°K.

The discussion of the results will be postponed to § 7.

c) C e s i u m   a l u m i n i u m   a l u m. Figure 13 shows the relaxation time for protons in $CsAl(SO_4)_2 . 12H_2O$ with Ti^{+++} ions as impurity. The ratio Al : Ti was 40 : 1. The powder sample was made from clear crystals of about 3 mm diameter. There is now a minimum in the curve for T_1. This difference, compared to the case of Cr impu-

Fig. 14. The relaxation time T_1 for the proton resonance at 30.5 Mc/sec in $ZnSO_4 . 7H_2O$ with various amounts of Ni^{++} impurities as a function of temperature.

rities, is related to the different magnetic behaviour of the two ions, as will be shown later.

d. Zinc sulphate heptahydrate. We made three samples containing different amounts of Ni-impurities.

❦❦

I contained "pure" $ZnSO_4.7H_2O$, in II 0.078% Ni was added (Zn : Ni = 260 : 1) and III contained 0.65% Ni (Zn : Ni = 30 : 1). The relaxation time of the proton resonance at 30.5 Mc/sec is plotted against the absolute temperature in fig. 14.

e. Copper sulphate pentahydrate. The relaxation time for protons in a single crystal of $CuSO_4.5H_2O$ was shorter than 0.01 sec even at 1.1°K. The system of proton spins could not be saturated with the available power.

f. Alkalihalides. The resonance of Li^7 and F^{19} has been observed at 9.5 Mc/sec in a powder of LiF (K a h l b a u m), that contained 0.074% of iron. The values for T_1 at 2.1°K are 10 sec for F^{19} and 35 sec for Li^7. The Li^7 resonance was also observed in the same sample of LiCl, that G o r t e r and B r o e r [10]) used in their early attempt to detect nuclear magnetic resonance. The relaxation time was 10 minutes at 2.1°K. When G o r t e r and B r o e r hit the resonance they probably saturated the sample immediately and when passing the resonance line again in order to check the probably observed abrupt change of frequency, this did not reproduce. This may explain their negative result. Another, less pure, sample of LiCl had values T_1 = 7 sec. at 14°K and T_1 = 90 sec. at 2.1°K. Both the Na^{23} and F^{19} resonance were observed at 9.5 Mc/sec. in a powder of NaF. The relaxation times are 100 sec. at 2.1°K and 180 sec. at 1.2°K for Na^{23}, and 15 sec. at 2.1°K and 1.1°K for F^{19}. The same powder was molten in a platinum crucible with a hydrogen flame and cooled rapidly. By this treatment probably many colour centers were formed in the crystals, or perhaps the formation of hydrides occurred because of the diffusion of hydrogen [27]). At any rate, the results for the relaxation time after this treatment were completely different and are given in the table.

TABLE II

	14°K	2.1°K	1.2°K
Na^{23}	0.6 sec	1.1 sec	3 sec
F^{19}	15	20	45

It is seen that T_1 for fluorine at 2°K increased by a small factor, but at the same time T_1 for sodium decreased by a factor of about 100. The discussion of this peculiar result will be deferred to § 7.

In a single, clear, crystal of NaCl no Na^{23} resonance could be

✦✦✦

detected at 2.1°K, after the sample had been kept in the magnetic field for two hours. We infer from this that $T_1 > 10^4$ sec.

The line width in these crystals is in agreement with (3). The widest lines (≈ 20 oersted) occur in LiF, while in LiCl the line is only about 5 oersted wide.

Fig. 15. The theoretical behaviour of T_1 for the proton resonance in $KAl(SO_4)_2 . 12H_2O$ containing different amounts of Cr-impurities. These values of T_1 should compared with the experimental results in figure 12.

4. *Theory of the relaxation mechanism.* We have to consider the system of nuclear spins s in combination with the system of impurity spins ω. The Hamiltonian for the problem may be written as

$$H = H_0 + H_L - \mathbf{H}_0 . \mathbf{M}_S + H_{LO} + H_{SO} + H_{SS} + H_{SI} - \mathbf{H}_0 . \mathbf{M}_I + H_{II} \quad (4)$$

H_0 is the orbital energy of the impurity in the crystalline field,

H_L is the energy of the lattice vibrations,

$- \mathbf{H}_0 . \mathbf{M}_S$ is the total magnetic energy of the impurity in the external field $\mathbf{H}_0$,

H_{LO} is the interaction between lattice vibrations and orbits,

H_{SO} represents the spin-orbit coupling,

H_{SS} is the spin-spin interaction between impurities which, besides the magnetic dipole-dipole coupling, may contain an exchange energy.

All these terms together refer to the system of impurities alone and have been discussed by several authors [11] [12]), especially V a n V l e c k [13]).

The last two terms of (4) refer to the system of nuclear spins only and have been discussed in detail in l.c.:

$$- \mathbf{H}_0 . \mathbf{M}_I = - \mathbf{H}_0 . \underset{i}{\Sigma} \gamma_i \hbar \mathbf{I}_i \qquad (5)$$

is the total magnetic energy of the nuclear spins in the external field.

$$H_{II} = \underset{j>i}{\Sigma} V_{ij} = \tfrac{1}{2} \underset{i}{\Sigma} \gamma_i \hbar \mathbf{I}_i \underset{j \mp i}{\Sigma} \left(\frac{\gamma_j \hbar \mathbf{I}_j}{r_{ij}^3} - \frac{3\gamma_j \hbar \mathbf{r}_{ij}(\mathbf{r}_{ij} . \mathbf{I}_i)}{r_{ij}^5} \right) \qquad (6)$$

is the nuclear magnetic spin-spin interaction. The interaction V_{ij} between a pair of dipoles may be written in the form appropriate for the m_i, m_j representation:

$$V_{ij} = \gamma_i \gamma_j \hbar^2 r_{ij}^{-3} (A + B + C + D + E + F) \qquad (7)$$

$A = I_{z_i} I_{z_j} (1 - 3 \cos^2 \vartheta_{ij}) \qquad \Delta m_i = \Delta m_j = 0$

$B = - \tfrac{1}{4} \left[(I_{x_i} - iI_{y_i}) (I_{x_j} + iI_{y_j}) + (I_{x_i} + iI_{y_i}) (I_{x_j} - iI_{y_j}) \right]$
$\qquad (1 - 3 \cos^2 \vartheta_{ij}) \qquad \Delta m_i = - \Delta m_j = \pm 1$

$C = - \tfrac{3}{2} \left[(I_{x_i} + iI'_{y_i}) I_{z_j} + (I_{x_j} + iI_{y_j}) I_{z_i} \right] \sin \vartheta_{ij} \cos \vartheta_{ij} \, e^{-i\varphi_{ij}} e^{+i\gamma H_0 t}$
$\qquad\qquad\qquad\qquad \Delta m_i = 1 \quad \Delta m_j = 0$
$\qquad\qquad\qquad\qquad \Delta m_i = 0 \quad \Delta m_j = 1$

$D = - \tfrac{3}{2} \left[(I_{x_i} - iI_{y_i}) I_{z_j} + (I_{x_j} + (I_x - iI_{y_j}) I_{z_i} \right] \sin \vartheta_{ij} \cos \vartheta_{ij} \, e^{+i\varphi_{ij}} e^{-i\gamma H_0 t}$
$\qquad\qquad\qquad\qquad \Delta m_i = - 1 \quad \Delta m_j = 0$
$\qquad\qquad\qquad\qquad \Delta m_i = 0 \qquad \Delta m_j = - 1$

$E = - \tfrac{3}{4} (I_{x_i} + iI_{y_i}) (I_{x_j} + iI_{y_j}) \sin^2 \vartheta_{ij} \, e^{-2i\varphi_{ij}} e^{+2i\gamma H_0 t}$
$\qquad\qquad\qquad\qquad \Delta m_i = \Delta m_j = 1$

$F = - \tfrac{3}{4} (I_{x_i} - iI_{y_i}) (I_{x_j} - iI_{y_j}) \sin^2 \vartheta_{ij} \, e^{+2i\varphi_{ij}} e^{-2i\gamma H_0 t}$
$\qquad\qquad\qquad\qquad \Delta m_i = \Delta m_j = - 1$

The term H_{SS} may be expanded into a similar form, although it will in general no longer be true that S_z contains only diagonal, and $S_x + iS_y$ only non-diagonal elements. For usually there is also an electrical splitting in the crystalline field.

The term H_{SI} represents the magnetic interaction between impurities and nuclear spins and may also be written in the form (7), if we replace I_j by S_j. In considering the impurities, H_{SI} may be neglected in comparison with the first four terms of (4), as this means only the omission of the reaction of the nuclear spins on the impurity. For the nuclear spin system represented by the last two terms of (4), H_{SI} will be shown to be an important perturbation.

It has been shown in l.c. for a system of nuclear spins only, how the terms C, D, E, and F of (7) provide a relaxation mechanism, when they are combined with the time variation of the space coordinates r and ϑ of the nuclei. The fundamental idea underlying Waller's theory [2] [3] [4] is that the time variations in the local field are caused by the lattice vibrations. A calculation on this basis gives the theoretical curve of fig. 1.

When impurities are included in the picture, one might at first be inclined to follow the same line of thought. The local field at the nuclei is now greatly enhanced by the term H_{SI}, the matrix elements of which are larger than those of H_{II} by a factor $\gamma_{el}/\gamma_{nucl.} \approx 10^3$. Therefore the nuclear relaxation time should be shorter by a factor 10^6. This explanation cannot be the correct one. In the first place comparison of figures 1 and 8 shows that the discrepancy is larger than a factor 10^5, secondly the variation of T_1 with temperature would remain wrong, and last but not least, the decrease of T_1 by a factor fo 10^6 would only be valid for those nuclei which are in the proximity of an impurity. But impurities are already effective in very small concentrations (see § 3), when most nuclei are so far away from them, that the factor r^{-3} in the matrix elements for the magnetic interatcion more than offsets the influence of $\gamma_{el}/\gamma_{nucl.}$.

The term H_{SI}, however, gives the required fluctuations in the local field near the impurity, if the time variations of the spin coordinate of the impurity is taken into account. So these nuclei have a good heat contact with the lattice via the impurity; the heat contact with the other nuclei will be discussed in the next paragraph. We shall assume for the moment that the term H_{SS} may be neglected. This seems certainly correct, when there is less than $10^{-2}\%$ impurity. The average distance between impurities is then larger than 10^2 Å and the local field which they produce at the position of one another less than 0.05 oersted.

In § 6 we shall discuss the influence of H_{SS} in the case of higher concentrations of impurities.

The system to be considered consists therefore of one impurity and a large number of nuclear spins around it. In the case of Al-alum, contaminated with $10^{-3}\%$ Cr (sample II) there are e.g. 5.10^5 protons for one Cr^{+++} ion. The average distance between two protons is roughly 2.5 Å and between two Cr^{+++} ions 200 Å.

The energy levels corresponding to $H_0' - \mathbf{H}_0.\mathbf{M}$ of a Cr-ion in a crystalline and magnetic field are known for KCr-alum [23]. We may assume that the situation is not drastically altered for the very diluted specimen in our case. There is evidence that the electric splitting parameter changes slightly on dilution. The influence of the terms H_{OL}' and H_{OS}' has been investigated in great detail by V a n   V l e c k. The lattice vibrations cause a fluctuating electric field, which distorts the orbital motion slightly. Via the spin-orbit coupling transitions are then induced between the four spin levels. This is the well known theory [13] of spin-lattice relaxation in paramagnetic salts. A detailed experimental investigation has been made by G o r t e r [14] and collaborators during the past twelve years. Especially the case of Cr-alum received much attention. The effect can be described in terms of a spin-lattice relaxation time ϱ which, in general, is a function of H_0 and the lattice temperature T. The quantity ϱ determines the average life time of the spin levels against transitions. This flopping of the impurity spin, caused by the coupling to the lattice, produces a large fluctuating local field at the surrounding nuclei. The space coordinates in the terms B, C, D, E and F of H_{SI}' may be regarded as time independent, but the expectation values of the components of the angular momentum operator $\mathbf{S}$ are functions of time. The intensity $J_z(\nu)$ of the Fourier spectra of the expectation values of the z-component of the magnetic moment $\gamma_{el}\hbar S_z$ may be defined, and also of the $x + iy$ components.

Diagonal elements of the operator $\mathbf{S}$ will contribute to the spectrum near frequency zero, non-diagonal elements to the spectrum around the frequency corresponding to the energy difference of the states they connect. The frequency range over which the intensity will be spread in each case is given by $\varDelta\nu \approx \varrho^{-1}$.

The relaxation time T_1 for a nuclear spin using the terms B, C and E of H_{SI}' is given by (compare formula (28) of l.c.)

$$1/2T_1 = W = \tfrac{9}{4}\gamma^2 r^{-6} \sin^2 \vartheta \cos^2 \vartheta J_z(\nu_0) +$$
$$+ \tfrac{9}{16}\gamma^2 r^{-6} \sin^4 \vartheta J_{x+iy}(\nu_0) +$$
$$+ \tfrac{1}{16}\gamma^2 r^{-6} (1 - 3 \cos^2 \vartheta)^2 J_{x-iy}(\nu_0) \qquad (8)$$

As the Larmor frequency ν_0 of the nuclei is so low (10^7 sec^{-1}) that

$h\nu_0$ is small compared to the spacing in energy of the impurity spin levels and usually $\varrho > 10^{-8}$ sec, only diagonal elements of $\mathbf{S}$ will contribute appreciably to the intensity at ν_0. When there is no splitting by electric fields (the case of Ti^{+++}) S_z will have only diagonal elements and $S_{x\pm iy}$ only nondiagonal elements. In this case we have, using the well known frequency distribution of D e b ij e corresponding to an average life time $\varrho/2\pi$

$$J_z(\nu_0) = \tfrac{1}{3}\gamma_{el}^2\, \hbar^2\, S(S+1)\, \varrho\pi^{-1}(1 + \varrho^2\nu_0^2)^{-1}. \tag{9}$$

It means that the correlation function for the expectation value of S_z is assumed to be an exponential function. In combination with (8) we have

$$1/T_1' = \tfrac{3}{2}\gamma_i^2\gamma_{el}^2\hbar^2 S(S+1)\, r^{-6} \sin^2\vartheta \cos^2\vartheta\,.\,\varrho\pi^{-1}(1+\varrho^2\nu_0^2)^{-1} = Cr^{-6}. \tag{10}$$

We neglect the angular dependence, then C is a constant depending on ϱ.

When an electric splitting occurs, only the numerical factors in (9) will change, but the order of magnitude of T_1' will still be given by (10). Substituting numerical values, $\gamma = 2.7 \times 10^4$ for protons, $\gamma_{el} = 2 \times 10^7$, $S = \tfrac{3}{2}$ for Cr^{+++} spins, $\varrho = 3.10^{-5}$ in Cr-alum at $77°$K, $\nu_0 = 3.10^{+7}$, we find $T_1' = 1$ sec. for protons which are 2.10^{-7} cm away from the impurity. This distance corresponds to a critical radius b, where the magnetic field from the impurity, $\gamma_{el}\hbar/b^3$ is about equal to the local field produced by the other nuclei. The nuclei inside this radius will have shorter relaxation times, but their resonance frequencies are shifted far into the wings of the absorption line because of the interaction A of H_{SI}. Futhermore their number is small, so that usually their resonance escapes observation. Most of the nuclei will be much further away than the radius b. In the most diluted sample of Al-alum (II) e.g. more than 90% of the protons are more than 10^2 Å away and would have relaxation times $T_1' > 1.5 \times 10^4$ sec. So far this theory cannot explain the observed relaxation time of 4 sec. in sample II at $77°$K, but there is another interaction.

5. *Spin diffusion.* Suppose we have a crystalline lattice of nuclear spins in a magnetic field H_0 and the temperature of the spin system at one end of the crystal be T_S, at the other end T_S', and we ask for how thermal equilibrium will be reached. The temperature T_S may

be defined at each lattice point in the case $I = \frac{1}{2}$ by

$$p = P_{\frac{1}{2}} - P_{-\frac{1}{2}} = \operatorname{tgh} \gamma \hbar H_0/2k\,T_S \approx \gamma \hbar H_0/2k\,T_S \tag{11}$$

where $P_{\frac{1}{2}}$ is the probability to find the nuclear spin oriented parallel to H_0, $m_z = +\frac{1}{2}$, and $P_{-\frac{1}{2}}$ is the probability to find for the z-component of the spin $m_z = -\frac{1}{2}$. The transfer of energy from the region with higher spin temperature to that with lower temperature is brought about by simultaneous transitions of antiparallel spins i and j, represented by term B of the nuclear magnetic interaction H'_{II}. The probability per unit time for such a process may be estimated on the basis of a rather naive picture. Consider first the interaction A of nuclei i and j with all other nuclei except with one another. The two nuclei will have slightly different Larmor frequencies, both varying with time because of the fluctuating local z-fields. The matrix elements of $I_{x_i} \pm I_{y_i}$ connecting the upper and lower level of spin i will spread around the frequency ν_0 over a range $2\pi \, \Delta\nu_i \approx 1/T_2$, and similarly for spin j. The maximum of the normalised frequency distribution function will be of the order of T_2, where T_2 is given by (3).

Now introduce the interaction B between i and j as a small perturbation. Using the standard perturbation expression for the probability to find a system in a state with $\Delta m_i = -\Delta m_j = 1$

$$\hbar^2 \mid B_{ij} \mid^2 \left| \frac{1 - e^{i(\Delta\omega_i - \Delta\omega_j)t}}{\Delta\omega_i - \Delta\omega_j} \right|^2$$

and integrating over the frequency distribution of $\Delta\omega_i$ and $\Delta\omega_j$ we obtain for the time proportional transition probability of an anti-parallel pair:

$$W_{\Delta m_i = -\Delta m_j = 1} = \frac{1}{16}\,\gamma^4\,\hbar^2\,r_{ij}^{-6}\,(1 - 3\cos^2\vartheta_{ij})^2\,\lambda T_2 \tag{12}$$

where λ is a numerical factor of the order of unity, depending upon the shape of the distribution function. Summing over all nuclei j one finds with (3) for a system of identical nuclei that the transition probability for one spin is given by

$$W_{\Delta m_i} \equiv 1/T_2''' = \lambda/18\,T_2.$$

This result is not at all surprising. The rate at which energy is exchanged between the spins should be given in order of magnitude by the inverse of the spin-spin relaxation time. K r o n i g and B o u w k a m p [15]) also calculated the probability that one spin

✦✦

makes a transition in a large magnetic field H_0. They found very long relaxation times, as they required that the total moment of the other spins remained unchanged. B r o e r [11]) has analyzed and critisized this matter in detail. Actually T_2''' is longer than T_2 by a numerical factor of the order 10, as $1/T_2$ measured the total width of the resonance, to which the interaction A also contributes. If there are also non-identical nuclei in the lattice, the ratio T_2'''/T_2 becomes larger. No exchange of energy between non-identical spins occurs. Different nuclear spin systems have no direct heat contact.

V a n V l e c k [9]) has calculated T_2 in a rigorous manner, considering the spin system as a whole. It does not seem easy to apply this method to the calculation of T_2''', which describes the energy transport in a system of which different parts have different temperatures. Therefore we adhere to a simple picture, in which all spins are considered separately. We want to point out two important limitations of our perturbation procedure. When the nuclei occur in pairs — like protons in the same watermolecule in hydrated salts — we cannot first exclude the interaction between this pair, as it is much stronger than all other interactions. P a k e [8]) has shown that this pair of spins combines to a triplet state and gives rise to a fine structure of the resonance line. The interaction between the various triplets could then be treated by the preceding method and produces an exchange of energy between proton pairs.

Furthermore our considerations are subject to the restriction $\gamma \hbar H_0 < kT$. When $\gamma \hbar H_0 \gg kT$, most spins will be parallel to H_0, the number of antiparallel pairs is reduced considerably and the local fields will not fluctuate so much that integration over $\Delta \omega_i$ is allowed. F r ö h l i c h and H e i t l e r [16]) have considered this case. An antiparallel spin is then treated as an excited particle which can travel freely through the lattice, only scattered in rare collisions with other excited particles. This picture reminds of Bloch's spin waves. In our case $\gamma \hbar H_0 \ll kT$, which is the only one of practical interest for nuclear spins, there are about as many excited particles as unexcited ones, and we may say that the "excitons" are scattered at each lattice point. We shall show that the situation may be described as a diffusion process in which the mean free path of the excited particles is a, the lattice constant, and the mean time between collision T_2'''. It is interesting to note that the formulae 17 and 31 B of H e i t l e r and F r ö h l i c h [16]) which, strictly speaking, are not applicable in this case where $U \ll kT$, give the same result, except for unimportant numerical factors

Let us assume for simplicity that the nuclei have a spin $I = \frac{1}{2}$ and lie on a simple cubic lattice and let us first consider the interaction between a spin and its six nearest neighbours, at distance a only, for the interaction drops as r^{-6}. Neglecting its angular dependence, we have for the probability for a simultaneous transition between neighbours from (12)

$$W \approx \tfrac{1}{50} T_2.$$

The numerical factor has, of course, only an order of magnitude significance. For the transport of $p = P_{\frac{1}{2}} - P_{-\frac{1}{2}}$ in the x-direction we have

$$-\frac{\partial p}{\partial t} = W \{P_{\frac{1}{2}}(x+a)\, P_{-\frac{1}{2}}(x) - P_{\frac{1}{2}}(x)\, P_{-\frac{1}{2}}(x-a) +$$
$$+ P_{\frac{1}{2}}(x-a)\, P_{-\frac{1}{2}}(x) - P_{\frac{1}{2}}(x)\, P_{-\frac{1}{2}}(x + a)\} \tag{13}$$

Making the transition to a differential equation and extending to three dimensions we find

$$-\frac{\partial p}{\partial t} = D\, \Delta p \tag{14}$$

where the diffusion constant is given by

$$D = Wa^2 \approx a^2/50\, T_2 \tag{15}$$

The situation is that of a random walk problem for the quantity p, the surplus fraction of nuclei in the state with lower energy. Although the transitions for nuclei which are not neighbours are less frequent, they cannot be neglected, as there are many more of them and as the quantity p is transported over a larger distance in such a process. One finds immediately that the sum of the contributions of all nuclei converges only as r^{-1}. Considering the angular dependence one finds that for an isotropic substance the diffusion constant in the direction of H_0 is 2.2 times larger than perpendicular to H_0. For a simple cubic lattice the contribution of the various nuclei to the random walk process has been examined in greater detail with (12). The result is that the diffusion, averaged over all directions, does not depend very much on the angle of H_0 and the crystal axes. If H_0 is parallel to the 1.1.1 direction, the nearest neighbours do not contribute to the diffusion nor to the line width, but for the average diffu-

+++

sion this effect is counterbalanced by the other neighbours. More precisely one finds that the ratio of the average values of DT_2 when H_0 1.1.1 and 1.0.0 direction respectively is 2.1, while the ratio for T_2 in these cases is 2.3. Substituting numerical values into (15), $a = 2 \times 10^{-8}$ cm, $T_2 = 10^{-5}$ sec, we find $D \approx 10^{-12}$ cm^2 sec^{-1}. The order of magnitude of the heat conductivity $\varkappa$ is obtained by multiplying D with the specific heat $\gamma^2 \hbar^2 I (I + 1) H_0^2 a^{-3}/3kT^2$ of the nuclear spin system; $\varkappa \approx 10^{-15}$ erg sec^{-1} cm^{-1} at room temperature. If we saturate the spin system at one end of a cm one long crystal (heating to a very high temperature by a large external r.f. field), it would take 10^{12} sec, before the temperature T_S at the other end would rise appreciably. The macroscopic heat conduction of the spin system is very small and inaccessible to measurements. But to transport the heat over, say 20, lattice distances, only 10^{-1} seconds are required. When we reconsider our model of one paramagnetic impurity, surrounded by a sphere of nuclear spins, we find that the diffusion plays an important role. The external radiation field tends to set up a temperature gradient in the spin system by saturating the nuclei far away from the impurity, while near it T_S will remain equal to the lattice temperature T_l. This effect is counteracted by the spin diffusion.

Let $W \approx \gamma^2 H_1^2 T_2$ be the transition probability of a spin in the external radiation field H_1, and Cr^{-6} twice the transition probability W_1 in the field of the impurity given by (10), then we have in combination with (14) the equation for the surplus fraction p

$$-\frac{\partial p}{\partial t} = D \, \Delta p + 2Wp + Cr^{-6} \, (p - p_0) \tag{16}$$

where p_0 is the surplus, when the spin temperature is equal to the lattice temperature. This equation reduces for the stationary state $\partial p / \partial t = 0$ to an ordinary differential equation of the second order which must be solved numerically. The following boundary conditions are imposed. We divide the crystal in spheres with equal radius R around each impurity as center. If N is the number of impurities per cc., we have $4\pi R_d/3 = N^{-1}$. In reality the impurities are distributed at random over the lattice. Our assumption of isolated spheres of equal volume is, of course, artificial. It has, however, analytical convenience and does not impair the order of magnitude calculation. For $r = R$ we have the condition $dp/dr = 0$. At the boundary there is no transport of heat and no gradient in temperature. For the other boundary condition we take $dp/dr = 0$ for $r = b$. This means that there is no diffusion to the inside of the critical radius. Here the Larmor frequencies of the nuclei vary largely in the strong local field of the impurity and conservation of energy in the reciprocal transitions is no longer warranted. We now ask for the value of $W_{\frac{1}{2}}$ of W, for which

$$\int_{r=b}^{r=R} p \, 4\pi r^2 \mathrm{d}r = \tfrac{1}{2} \int_{r=b}^{r=R} p_0 4\pi r^2 \mathrm{d}r \qquad (17)$$

Then the imaginary part of the nuclear susceptibility has fallen to 50% of its unsaturated value and this will occur for a value of the saturation parameter $s = WT_1 \approx 1$, so that $T_1 = 1/W_{\frac{1}{2}}$.

Equation (16) with $\partial p/\partial t = 0$ has been solved numerically by ,,het Mathematisch Centrum te Amsterdam'', for various values of the parameter C and the outer radius R, the latter corresponding to various concentrations of the impurity. It turned out that a singular solution of (16) exists which remains finite at $r = 0$ and of which the first five derivatives vanish at $r = 0$. This function satisfies the condition $\partial p/\partial r = 0$ at $r = b$ closely, although not rigorously. It is combined linearly with a solution of the homogeneous equation which vanishes as $\exp(-k/r^2)$ at $r = 0$, in such a way as to meet the boundary condition at $r = R$.

The value $W_{\frac{1}{2}}/D$, for which (17) is satisfied, was determined as a function of the parameters C/D and R.

If we assume that the protons in $KAl(SO_4)_2 . 12H_2O$ are located in a simple cubic lattice with constant $a = 2.5$ Å, we find that $R = 27.5$ Å, 60 Å and 125 Å respectively for sample II, III and IV. If we take furthermore $T_2 = 10^{-5}$ sec. and use the formula (10) to express C as a function of ϱ, we are able to plot the theoretical values of $T_1 = 1/W_{\frac{1}{2}}$ as a function of ϱ for various Cr^{+++} concentrations. This has been done in figure 15, which should be compared with the experimental results of figure 12.

The theory predicts that T_1 should be proportional to $N^{-1.1}\varrho^{0.3}$ for a large range of ϱ- and N-values. There is a satisfactory agreement between predicted and measured values of T_1 at 77°K, but the theoretical values are too short by a factor between 10 and 50 in the liquid helium range. This decrepancy will be discussed in § 7.

When the relaxation is observed on the oscilloscope with the direct method, we should solve the partial differential equation (16), where

꙳꙳꙳

now the term Wp may be neglected, and determine $\int_{r=b}^{r=R} p \, 4\pi r^2 dr$ as a function of time. This has not been carried out. Experimentally always an exponential function was found for the growth of the absorption curve within the limits of error (comp. figure 4) and we assumed that this characteristic time has the same value as that calculated in the preceding case. It is doubtful whether it is worth while to make more detailed calculations with our oversimplified model. The two important features of the theory, the heat contact with the lattice via the impurities and the diffusion of absorbed energy quanta toward the neighbourhood of the impurities, are clearly brought to light. The diffusion is completely independent of both the temperature of the lattice T_l and the external field H_0, but the first process is a rather sensitive function of these quantities, because formula (10) contains ϱ, which varies with T and H_0, and the Larmor frequency v_0, which is proportional to H_0. A detailed discussion and comparison with the experiment will be postponed to § 7.

Before we conclude this paragraph, the question should be raised how the nuclear spins in the sphere around the impurity can possibly "feel" the temperature of the one degree of freedom, the impurity spin. Furthermore it is questionable whether the spin temperautre T_S can be defined for each lattice point.

Especially in the neighbourhood of the impurity, where only a small number of nuclei is present, this point needs justification. In the derivation of the relaxation process, usually the ad hoc hypothesis is introduced [17] [1] that the transition probabilities arising from local fields are supplied with the Boltzmann factor of the final state so that they automatically establish thermal equilibrium.

It would be interesting in the present case to analyze the thermal statistical properties of the system in more detail. In such a theory the reaction of the nuclear spins on the impurity should certainly be included. An interesting experiment in this respect was suggested to thr author by Professor P u r c e l l. The temperature of the impurity spins may be raised above the lattice temperature by a strong field in the microwave region at the magnetic resonance of the electronic spins. Will the nuclear spins follow this temperature? A well established example of a system which has a heat contact through one degree of freedom is an evacuated galvanometer or

✦✦

electrometer system [18]), which assumes the temperature of the resistance providing the electrical damping.

6. *The interaction between impurities.* When the impurity content is high, it is not permissible to neglect the term H_{SS}, as we have done so far. We shall see later that this term may also become important for lower concentrations, e.g. in aluminium alum with $10^{-2}\%$ Cr below $4°K$.

But for the moment we restrict ourselves to the case of high impurity content (aluminium alum in which 5% or more of the Al-ions have been replaced by Cr-ions).

Then we can distinguish two systems of spins, one connected with the small nuclear magnetic moments, the other with the large moments of the impurities. The coupling between the two systems, represented by the term H_{SI}, may be considered as a small perturbation. The mechanism to be described is the transfer of the small energy quanta $h\nu_0$, absorbed by the nuclear spin from the radio-frequency field, to the system of impurity spins. This process is entirely independent of the lattice vibrations and would also occur in a spatially rigid lattice. The system of impurity spins absorbs the small quanta by rearrangement of the spins rather than by a change in the magnetic moment.

The impurities exchange their energy in much the same way as was described in the preceding paragraph for the nuclear spins. When there is no splitting by electrical fields, the situation is identical. The problem consists in calculating the frequency spectrum of the $x + iy$ component of the local field at the position of a nucleus i. This field is represented by expressions like $\sum_j \gamma_{el} \hbar S_{zj} r_{ij}^{-3} \sin \vartheta_{ij} \cos \vartheta_{ij}$ (compare eq. (8)) and fluctuates in virtue of the processes B in the system of impurity spins S_j, even when there are no lattice vibrations.

V a n   V l e c k [9]) and   B r o e r [11]) have developed a rigorous method to obtain information about the spectral distribution of $\sum_j S_j$ We are, however, more interested in the spectral distribution function for a single spin, since a nucleus i will in general be much closer to one impurity than to all others and the factor r_{ij}^{-3} makes the influence of the latter negligible. We have shown in the preceding section that one spin will make transitions at a rate of which the order of magnitude is given by the inverse spin-spin relaxation time

$$1/\varrho' \approx \gamma^2 \hbar r^{-3} \tag{18}$$

where r is the distance between nearest neighbours. We are interested in the spectral intensity at the resonance frequency of the nuclei and one might be inclined to use formula (10), where ϱ is replaced by ϱ'.

$$1/T_1'' \approx 1/T_1' \cdot \frac{1 + \varrho^2 v_0^2}{1 + \varrho'^2 v_0^2} \cdot \frac{\varrho'}{\varrho} \tag{19}$$

It is, however, not at all certain that the frequency spectrum should now also have the shape corresponding to a finite life time of the levels. The shape of the distribution function remains an unsolved problem.

Still more difficult to solve would be the following problem. In most cases of experimental interest the density of impurities is so low that the interaction H_{SS} is smaller than the interaction of the impurity with the surrounding nuclear spins H_{SI}. Then we cannot follow the treatment of two systems of spins with a small interaction because the system of impurity spins cannot be defined seperately from the nuclear spins. Nevertheless it is possible also in this case that small quanta, which have diffused through the nuclear spin system toward the impurity, are transferred to the system of large spins without the aid of the lattice vibrations. At low temperatures this temperature — independent process may become more rapid than that described in § 5, when the relaxation time ϱ is very long. The energy is transferred from the large spins to the lattice in the form of large quanta, a rapid process. It should be noted that the heat capacity of the impurity system is larger than that of the nuclear spins, even in very dilute salts.

When there is only one impurity on 10^5 nuclear spins, the heat capacities have the same order of magnitude. The considerations of this paragraph are again restricted by the condition $\gamma_{el} \hbar H_0 < kT$, which is usually valid under experimental conditions. When $\gamma_{el} \hbar H_0 \gg kT$ the picture of the travelling spins waves would become more appropriate.

When there is an electric splitting of the impurity levels, e.g. the case of Cr^{+++}, the $2S + 1$ spin levels in a magnetic field H_0 will not be equidistant. Therefore the number of simultaneous transitions, for which the energy is conserved, is reduced by a numerical factor. Furthermore will S_z contain also nondiagonal elements. Formula (19) should therefore be supplied with a numerical factor smaller than one but which will be of little importance in the order of magnitude calculation. It is possible however, for certain orientations of a single alum crystal in the field H_0, that two impurity spin levels cross each other, when plotted as a function of H_0. For certain values of H_0 the distance between the two spin levels could then be equal to the nuclear spin quanta $h\nu_0$ and for these values of H_0 a particularly short nuclear relaxation time might be expected. The reader should be cautioned that our ϱ' is not identical with that of B r o e r. His ϱ', which is a measure for the non-resonant spin absorption of the impurities decreases, when an electric splitting occurs.

The dependence of ϱ' on the concentration of impurities N may be derived from formula (3). When the impurities were evenly spaced, so that dilution would merely consist of an increase in the constant of the impurity lattice, $\varrho' \sim N^{-1}$. But a random distribution of the impurities in the diluted crystals is more conform the experimental conditions and then one finds immediately $\varrho' \sim N^{-\frac{1}{2}}$

When the impurity content is high (Cr : Al > 0.05) a large fraction of the nuclei will experience a magnetic z-field, which is considerably different from the external field H_0. The line will be broadened. If we use the instantaneous fields of the impurities, the line width in pure chrome alum should be about 600 oersted wide and so unobservable. Experimentally a trace of a 100 oersted wide line was found. In this case ϱ' is certainly so small that $\varrho'/T_2 \ll 1$, the local field will "average out" to some extent. This effect will be more pronounced when besides the magnetic interaction, there is a strong exchange as e.g. in $CuSO_4 . 5H_2O$. Here the Cu^{++} ions contribute negligibly to the line width. If one knows the frequency spectrum of $\Sigma \, S_{z_j} . r_{ij}^{-3} \, (1 - \cos^2 \vartheta_{ij})$, one may calculate the contribution of the impurities to the line width with formula (35) of l.c.

V a n   V l e c k [9]) also considered the influence of paramagnetic impurities on the line width of the nuclear resonance with the rigorous diagonal sum method and gives more precise formulae for the exchange narrowing. He arrives, however, at the conclusion that the line should already be broadened, when there is one impurity on 10^5 nuclear spins. This is clearly in contradiction with the experimental results. Van Vleck's conclusion about the increase of $[(\Delta\nu)^2_{Av}]^{\frac{1}{2}}$ is correct for the average over all lattice points j.

But as has been frequently pointed out above, the lattice points for the nuclear spins are far from aequivalent. The nuclei near the

✦✦

impurity have a large $(\Delta v)^2_{Av}$. But these are only a relatively small number.

When the ratio of the number of impurity spins to nuclear spins is smaller than 10^{-4}, most lattice points j will have a value $(\Delta v)^{\frac{1}{2}}_{Av}$, which is not appreciably different from the value calculated when there are no impurity spins at all. We conclude therefore that a broadening will occur only if the ratio of the numbers of the two types of spins is 10^{-3} or more and if the narrowing effect of magnetic or exchange interaction is not predominant. This view is corroborated by the experimental fact that the proton resonance line in KAl(Cr) $(SO_4)_2$. $12H_2O$ is broadened by a factor 1.3 only in sample V, where the ratio Cr : H = 1 : 700.

7. *Discussion of the results.* a) P o t a s s i u m   a l u m i n i u m   a l u m   w i t h   c h r o m e   i m p u r i t i e s. We start with this salt, as the nature of the impurities is best known in this case. Comparison of the experimental results for the diluted samples II, III and IV, contained in figures 11 and 12, with the theoretical curves of figure 15, shows that there is a reasonable agreement, both as to order of magnitude of T_1 at 77°K and as to the dependence of T_1 on the concentration N.

The latter can be described by $T_1 \sim N^a$, where a varies between —0.8 and —1.2, while theoretically $a = -1.1$ is predicted. Both the theoretical and experimental dependence of T_1 and ϱ is given by $T_1 \sim \varrho^\beta$, but the value of β derived from experiment ranges from 0.5 to 0.7, while theoretically $\beta = 0.3$ is predicted. This involves considerable discrepancies between theory and experiment at very low temperatures.

It should be remembered that the theoretical model was a rather crude approximation and that in the mathematical solution of (16) the decrease of the diffusion constant D inside the critical radius b was not taken into account. Furthermore the possibility cannot be excluded that the dependence of the constant C on ϱ is not given precisely by (10). At helium temperatures we are interested in the very tail of the distribution and it is questionable whether $C \sim \varrho^{-1}$ is rigorously correct.

Then there is some uncertainty what values of ϱ should be taken, as there is still considerable discrepancy between Van Vleck's theory [13]) and experimental results for the spin lattice relaxation time ϱ, especially at low temperatures. We have preferred to take the values of ϱ from measurements on pure chrome alum, carried out by B r o e r [11]) at 77°K, by D e V r ij e r [20]) at 20°K and by B ij l [21]) between 1.9°K and 4°K.

Since our field is 7000 $\varnothing$, we have used values of ϱ_∞ given by these authors: $\varrho_\infty = 3.10^{-6}$ sec. at 77°K, $\varrho_\infty = 2.10^{-4}$ sec. at 20°K, $\varrho_\infty = 8.10^{-3}$ sec. at 4.0°K.

It should be noted that the values of ϱ in diluted samples [22]) may differ by as much as a factor 3 from those in pure Cr-alum. This may partially be due to a different parameter of the electrical splitting [23]), and partly to the dipole-dipole interaction becoming negligible. The ϱ-values have been measured only in samples in which the ratio of Cr : Al was 0.05 or more and are not very well reproducible. The use of the values mentioned above has only an order of magnitude significance. The only way to obtain more reliable data for comparison with theory would be to carry out measurements of ϱ in the same samples as the nuclear resonance is observed. This would be rather difficult for the extremely diluted salts we have used. One might obtain values of ϱ from saturation effects of the paramagnetic resonance of Cr-ions in the centimeter region. Especially at low temperatures this method should be accurate and applicable to low Cr-concentrations. For the moment one should be satisfied with a qualitative agreement, which is even better than could be expected from the approximate character of the diffusion theory and the used ϱ-values.

It is clear, however, that samples III and IV do not agree with the theory of § 5 at a few degrees absolute. The relaxation time tends to a constant value (20 sec. for sample III, about 1500 sec. for IV). The explanation is proposed that the direct temperature independent heat contact with the impurity, described in § 6, begins to prevail.

In sample V the relaxation time is constant in the whole temperature, range, 5.10^{-3} sec. The experimental data are not very accurate, because only an onset of saturation could be observed, at all temperatures. The impurity content is so high, that the direct heat contact with the impurity system prevails even at room temperature. No diffusion of nuclear spins is necessary, as practically all nuclei are close to an impurity. In fact the Larmor frequency of many nuclei is shifted far into the wings of the resonance line. We shall direct our attention to the part contributing to the center of the line. The local field by the impurities for these nuclei is not larger than 15 oersted. We take for ϱ' in this diluted substance 5.10^{-9} sec.

Applying formula (10) and (19) with $\gamma_{el}^2 \hbar^2 S(S + 1)r^{-6} = 225$ oersted^2 we find $T_1 \approx 10^{-2}$ sec., which is the same order of magnitude as the experimental value.

Finally we discuss the influence of variation of H_0. The data taken at 9.5 Mc/sec., when compared to those at 30.5 Mc/sec. show the changes in T_1', when H_0 is lowered by a factor 3.4. The relaxation time in V remains practically unchanged in agreement with formula (19) for we have the case $\varrho'\nu_0 \ll 1$ and ϱ' is independent of H_0.

The independence of temperature of T_1 at low temperatures in samples III and IV is now even more pronounced. The asymptotic values T_1'' are 1.5 sec. and 200 sec. respectively. The inverse proportionality to the square of the concentration remains and T_1'' seems to be proportional to H_0^2. We were not able to calculate T_1'' in these cases of a very dilute system of impurities, but it is reasonable that smaller quanta are more readily absorbed by a rearrangement of the impurity spins. It is seen that the asymptotic value is reached at higher temperatures at 9.5 Mc/sec. than at 30.5 Mc/sec.

Unfortunately we could not extend the measurements at 9.5 Mc/sec. above 20°K because of an unfavorable signal to noise ratio, but the curves II and III in figures 9 and 10 indicate that T_1 in the region around 10°K is about proportional to H_0. Since we have from (10) and figure 12 that for $\varrho\nu_0 \gg 1$, $T_1 \sim C^{-0.5} \sim \varrho^{\frac{1}{2}}\nu_0$, this means that ϱ should be independent of H_0 at 14°K. The dependence of ϱ on H_0 has been subject of much controversy [21] [22]. In pure chrome alum ϱ increases with H_0 at all temperatures. Van Vleck's theory claims that ϱ should decrease with H_0 at helium temperatures.

B ij l finds experimentally that the dependence of ϱ in a diluted alum (Al : Cr = 13 : 1) has the right sign at 2°K, although there is no quantitative agreement with theory. It is to be expected that in our very dilute salts ϱ will more closely obey Van Vleck's calculations. It is not at all impossible that ϱ is indeed practically independent of H_0 in the range around 10°K. At very low temperatures, however, $\varrho \sim H_0^{-2}$ should be expected and therefore T_1 should be independent of H_0. But here T_1'' is usually shorter than T_1', so that the latter escapes observation.

b) Z i n c s u l p h a t e w i t h N i i m p u r i t i e s. The samples II and III of this salt had a concentration of Ni which is about a factor 2 higher than the Cr-concentration in the samples IV and V of aluminium alum. It is seen at once that the pure $ZnSO_4 . 7H_2O$ was less pure than the alum. The contamination is probably Fe^{++}.

We note the following differences when we compare figs. 9 and 14. There is no indication of an approach to an asymptotic value T_1'' in the latter. Even Ni III, which has about the same degree of contamination as Cr V, does not tend to a constant value; T_1 in Ni II is shorter by a factor of about 10 than in Cr IV. At higher temperatures between 77°K and 300°K the curve T_1 versus T seems to reach a minimum. The last two facts can be explained by noting, that the spin lattice relaxation time ϱ for Ni^{++} [11]) in $NiSO_4 . 7H_2O$ at 77°K is 10^{-7} sec., or 30 times shorter than for Cr^{+++} in Cr-alum. At 77°K T_1 for Ni II is seven times shorter than for Cr IV. According to (10) and figure 12, T_1 should be proportional to $\varrho^{0.5} N^{-1}$. Allowing for a small correction factor, because the diagonal elements of the magnetic moment operator for Ni^{++} are smaller than for Cr^{+++} (compare Table III of l.c.), one finds that the behaviour of Ni-ions can be explained satisfactorily by the theory. Experimental data for ϱ on Ni^{++} at other temperatures are not available but it is very likely that ϱ remains much shorter at all temperatures. It is likely that ϱ assumes a value $3 . 10^{-8}$ sec. between 77°K and 300°K. Then (10) predicts a minimum for T_1. As T_1 remains rather short at helium temperatures it is not surprising that sample II does not show a bend to the asymptotic value. We would expect, however, that T_1'' would become shorter than T_1' in sample III. The ϱ' in this salt is somewhat longer than in Cr V, as Ni^{++} has a smaller magnetic moment. Also the electric splitting of the Ni^{++} ion is somewhat different. If ϱ' is longer than in Cr V by a factor 4, everything might be explained because comparison of Cr IV and Cr V, which differ only by a factor 13 in impurity concentration, shows how very sensitive T_1 is in this transition region where H_{SS} is becoming more important than H_{IS}.

c) Cesium aluminium alum with Ti^{+++} impurity. This salt shows the same behaviour of the curve T_1 versus T as the Ni-salts. The minimum is more pronounced and occurs at about 20°K. This is at least in qualitative agreement with VanVleck's predictions [13]) on CsTi-alum in a field of 10^4 oersted: at 77°K $\varrho = 10^{-9}$ sec., at 1.2°K $\varrho = 1.8 \times 10^{-2}$ sec. Van den Han-

✦✦

d e l [31]) remarks, however, that experimental results on this salt are always somewhat dubious because of its chemical instability.

d) C o p p e r   s u l p h a t e   p e n t a h y d r a t e. In this substance there is a direct coupling between proton and copper spins. The intensity of the local field spectrum of the Cu^{++} ions is completely different from the cases discussed so far, as a strong exchange between Cu^{++} ions occurs [9] [24] [25]). The intensity of the spectrum at 30 Mc/sec. is apparently large enough to keep the nuclear relaxation time below 10^{-2} sec., while the intensity is small enough at low frequencies to keep the nuclear resonance lines narrow. These two conditions can easily be fulfilled simultaneously (compare e.g. the case of glycerin in l.c.). More details on this interesting substance regarding the fine structure of the proton resonance line may be found elsewhere [26]).

e) C a l c i u m   f l u o r i d e. A look at figure 8 reveals the phenomenon, not met in the other cases, that T_1 is independent of temperature in the single crystals between 300°K and 20°K. In the powder sample IV T_1 increases over the whole temperature range. The impurity in all cases is analysed as iron, but the relaxation time in the single crystals is larger by a factor 10^3 in some cases, although they contain only 10 times less iron. When a single crystal is powdered, the T_1 does not change; so a mechanical-structural effect is excluded. The explanation is probably that the impurities in natural single crystals are lumped into limited areas, while they are distributed at random in artificially made substances. This phenomenon is also known from the optical quality of natural and artificial alkali halogenide crystals. Now it follows at once from the diffusion theory that not only the chemical percentage of impurity is important, but also its distribution over the lattice. When impurities lump together, the spin diffusion will become the exclusively limiting factor and a temperature independent relaxation time is expected, which is longer than would be the case for well dispersed impurities. At lower temperatures T_1 may rise, when the process represented by formula (10) becomes a limiting factor. T_1 should be independent of H_0 in the first region, which is only approximately verified by measurements at 9.5 Mc/sec at 20°K. Below 14°K, T_1 changes about proportional to H_0, as we also found for aluminium alum. A further discussion seems irrelevant, as nothing is known about the coupling of Fe impurities to the CaF_2 lattice. The result that T_1 is independent of the orientation of the crystal axes with respect to H_0 at all tempera-

↯↯

tures, has been explained in § 5 for the diffusion process. Also the coupling to the impurity will not be sensitive to crystal orientation, as at the critical radius b the crystal may practically be considered as a continuous isotropic medium.

f) A l k a l i h a l i d e s. The diffusion constant D for two geometrically identical spin systems is proportional to $\gamma^4 I(I + 1)/T_2$. Since the line breadth in oersted for the Li^7 and F^{19} resonance in LiF is about the same, we have $D \sim \gamma^3 I(I + 1)$. The heat contact with an impurity is proportional to γ^2. We would expect the relaxation time for the F^{19} resonance in LiF to be shorter by a factor of at least $(\gamma_F/\gamma_{Li})_2 = 6$ than for Li^7, and in NaF a factor $\gamma_F^2/\gamma_{Na}^2 = 14$ shorter than for Na^{23}. Experimentally only factors of 3.5 and 7 were found respectively. The coupling to the impurity then seems to be different for the two ions. Unfortunately the nature of the impurity is unknown. The result of the treatment of the NaF powder by melting it in a hydrogen flame is very striking. The ratio of the relaxation times of Na^{23} and F^{19} becomes 0.05 instead of 7. It clearly shows that there is no heat contact between the two spin systems. The result could be understood, if the impurity consists of colloidal metallic sodium [27]), to which only the sodium nuclei in the NaF lattice are coupled, while the relaxation time in metals is known to be short by the magnetic interaction with conduction electrons [29]). Another explanation might be suggested, that the impurity has such a nature (e.g. an electron jumping to different positions around a positive hole [28])), that it produces an inhomogeneous electric field which interacts with the quadrupole moment of Na^{23}. However, only experiments with well defined impurities could solve this problem.

Although both theory and exepriment could be refined, as was indicated in this paper on many occasions, it seems doubtful whether an effect, which clearly depends only on impurities, could ever get beyond the stage of an order of magnitude agreement between theoretical and experimental results.

In order to detect nuclear resonances and to measure gyromagnetic ratios, one should never use too pure samples.

The fact that the relaxation time in samples with a high impurity content, like $CuSO_4.5H_2O$ and $KAl(Cr)(SO_4)_2.12H_2O$ (Cr : Al 0.01) tends to a constant, relatively short, value at very low temperatures makes these substances suitable to detect nuclear resonance in the region between 01°K and 1°K.

✦✦

For nuclear adiabatic demagnetisation the resonance in metals is perhaps still most promising [29]).

The author is indebted to Professor C. J. G o r t e ɪ and Professor H. A. K r a m e r s for many stimulating discussions and to Dr. K. W. T a c o n i s and the technical staff of this Laboratory for advice and aid in the low temperature work and construction of the cryostat.

This work is part of the research programme of the "Stichting voor Fundamenteel Onderzoek op het Gebied van de Materie" and was made possible by a financial support from the "Stichting voor Zuiver Wetenschappelijk Onderzoek".

Received January 14th, 1949.

REFERENCES

1) N. B l o e m b e r g e n, E. M. P u r c e l l and R. V. P o u n d, Phys Rev. **73**, 679, 19 48.
2) N. B l o e m b e r g e n, Thesis, Leiden, 1948.
3) W. H e i t l e r and E. T e l l e r, Proc. Roy. Soc. *A* **155**, 629, 1936.
4) I. W a l l e r, Z. Phys. **79**, 370, 1932.
5) R. V. P o u n d, Phys. Rev. **73**, 523, 1948.
6) B. V. R o l l i n, et al., Nature **160**, 436, 1947.
7) B. V. R o l l i n and J. H a t t o n, Phys. Rev. **74**, 346, 1948.
8) G. E. P a k e, J. Chem. Phys. **16**, 327, 1948.
9) J. H. v a n V l e c k, Phys. Rev. **74**, 1168, 1948.
10) C. J. G o r t e r and L. J. F. B r o e r, Physica **9**, 591, 1942.
11) L. J. F. B r o e r, Thesis, Amsterdam, 1945.
12) R. K r o n i g, Physica **6**, 33, 1939.
13) J. H. v a n V l e c k, Phys. Rev. **57**, 426, 1940.
14) C. J. G o r t e r, Paramagnetic Relaxation, Elsevier, Amsterdam 1947.
15) R. K r o n i g and C. J. B o u w k a m p, Physica **5**, 521, 1938.
16) H. F r ö h l i c h and W. H e i t l e r, Proc. Roy. Soc. *A* **155**, 640, 1936.
17) C. J. G o r t e r and R. K r o n i g, Physica **3**, 1009, 1936.
18) J. M. W. M i l a t z and J. J. v a n Z o l i n g e n, Physica (in press).
19) J. H. v a n V l e c k, J. Chem. Phys. **5**, 320, 1937.
20) F. W. d e V r ij e r, Thesis, Leiden, 1949.
21) H. B. G. C a s i m i r, D. B ij l and F. K. D u P r é, Physica **8**, 449, 1941; D. B ij l and H. C. K r a m e r s, unpublished data.
22) D. B ij l, Physica **8**, 495, 1941.
23) C. A. W h i t m e r, R. T. W e i d n e r, J. S. H s i a n g and P. R. W e i s s, Phys. Rev. **74**, 1478, 1948.
24) C. J. G o r t e r and J. H. v a n V l e c k, Phys. Rev. **72**, 1128, 1947.
25) D. M. S. B a g g u l e y, J. H. E. G r i f f i t h s and M. H. L. P r y c e, Nature **162**, 538, 1948.
26) N. B l o e m b e r g e n, Meeting of the Am. Phys. Soc., New York, 1949.
27) R. W. P o h l, Phys. Z. **39**, 36, 1939.
28) N. F. M o t t and R. W. G u r n e y, Electronic Processes in ionic crystals, Oxford 1940.
29) N. B l o e m b e r g e n, Physica (in press).
30) G. E. P a k e and H. S. G u t o w s k i, Phys. Rev. **74**, 979, 1948.
31) J. v a n d e n H a n d e l. Thesis, Leiden.

COMMENTS AND CORRECTIONS

Since the material in the thesis was written at a time when less than one per cent of the present literature was available, it is clear that the following comments cannot change it into an up-to-date account. The reader interested in a modern, rigorous exposition of the theory of nuclear magnetic relaxation and the principal experiments are referred to the treatise by A. Abragam, "The Principles of Nuclear Magnetism," Oxford University Press, New York, 1961. It may nevertheless be helpful to point out to what extent the material presented here can stand on its own feet, even today.

The following list, arranged in numerical order of the pages, contains the locations where the text would need major revision, as well as a number of annoying minor errors. (Ignore equations when counting lines.)

5   3rd line from top: The paper alluded to is N. Bloembergen, E. M. Purcell, and R. V. Pound, Phys. Rev., **73**, 679 (1948), often referred to in the literature as BPP.

9   7th line from bottom: Omit "a."

10   10th line from bottom: Reference K5 has a new edition and should now read, "Nuclear Moments," Academic Press, New York, 1958.

14   Eq. (1.5): The last two terms should be preceded by minus signs.

17   Eq. (1.13): Read "$w_{m' \leftarrow m}$" instead of "$w_{m \leftarrow m'}$."

19   Lines 3 to 6: More-up-to-date references to the field of molecular beams, including tables of nuclear moments, are: N. F. Ramsey, "Molecular Beams," Oxford University Press, New York, 1956; P. Kusch and V. W. Hughes, "Encyclopedia of Physics," vol. 37 (1), 1, Springer-Verlag, Berlin, 1959.

20   21st line from top: Read "absorption" instead of "absorbtion."

23   5th line from top: Read "and" instead of "aud."
    6th line from bottom: Read "$\omega_0 = -\gamma H_0$" instead of "$\omega_0 = \gamma H_0$."

24   8th and 14th lines from top: Read "$\vec{H}' + \vec{\omega}/\gamma$" instead of "$\vec{H}' - \vec{\omega}/\gamma$."

173

24   Eq. (2.5): Read "$(\vec{\omega}/\gamma) + H_0$" instead of "$-\omega/\gamma + H_0$."

27   3rd line from bottom: Read "if" instead of "is."

28   11th line from bottom: Read "frequencies" instead of "frequences."

29   Eq. (2.24): The first term on the right-hand side should have a minus sign. Add a closing parenthesis to the numerator of the last term $(\vec{r}_{ij} \cdot \vec{I}_j)$. Modern treatments also include a scalar spin coupling of the form $\sum_{ij} A_{ij} \vec{I}_j \cdot \vec{I}_j$, mentioned in the third paragraph on this page.

31   5th line from top: Read "has a sharp" instead of "has sharp."

     11th line from top: Read "$(E_p - E_q)/h$" instead of "$E_p - E_q/h$."

     Eq. (2.26): Read "ρ_p" instead of "ρ_q."

32   18th line from bottom: Omit "the."

34   Last two equations: The terms E and F should be preceded by minus signs.

37   11th line from top: Read "distinguish" instead of "distingiush."

38-41   The correct way to describe the relaxation by dipole-dipole interaction is to consider a pair of spins rather than a single spin i. Solomon [Phys. Rev., 99, 559 (1955)] has considered the relaxation of a pair of (identical or nonidentical) spins, both with $I = 1/2$. He introduces four populations N^{++}, N^{+-}, N^{-+}, N^{--} for the four possible combinations of spin quantization.

     The difficulty with our treatment resides in the processes E and F, when two spins flip simultaneously. These processes should have a Boltzmann factor with an exponent that is a factor two larger than allowed for in Eq. (2.44). The result is that the term $J_2(2\nu_0)$ in Eq. (2.53) should be multiplied by a factor two. The correct result was first given by Kubo and Tomita [J. Phys. Soc. Japan, 9, 888 (1954)].

     Furthermore, Eq. (2.44) contains two misprints and should have read:

$$\frac{dN^+}{dt} = -WN^+ \exp\left(\frac{\gamma \hbar H_0}{kT}\right) + WN^- \exp\left(-\frac{\gamma \hbar H_0}{kT}\right)$$

42   8th line from top: Read "two" instead of "to."

42-44   Whereas the treatment of T_1, apart from the correction noted above, is essentially correct, the treatment of T_2 needs major revision. Solomon [Phys. Rev., 99,

559 (1955)] introduces the populations of four states with transverse magnetization. These states are linear combinations of eigenstates with different m values. This concept gives immediate physical insight into the nature of the decay of the transverse components of magnetization.

A more elegant and comprehensive theoretical formulation uses the concept of the density matrix. The time variation of the diagonal elements of this matrix determines one or more longitudinal relaxation times T_1, the time variation of the off-diagonal elements the transverse relaxation times T_2. In his book Abragam gives a coherent and complete account of the theory, based on original papers of Kubo and Tomita [J. Phys. Soc. Japan, **9**, 888 (1954)], Bloch [Phys. Rev., **102**, 104 (1956)], and Redfield [IBM J. Research, **1**, 19 (1957)].

It can be shown rigorously, in the limit of rapid motion, that the line shape is Lorentzian. Complete expressions which should replace Eq. (2.58) may be found in Chapter 8 of Abragam's book.

The discussion on page 42 gives physical insight into the change in line shape when the motion slows down to that of a rigid lattice. It is remarkable that the simple argument gives such a good qualitative account of the physical situation. The reader is referred to Chapter 10 of Abragam's book for a more elaborate treatment, based on the work of Kubo and Tomita [J. Phys. Soc. Japan, **9**, 888 (1954)] and Anderson [J. Phys. Soc. Japan, **9**, 316 (1954)].

46   9th line from top: Read "... as v for $T_2 \Delta \omega = (1 + \gamma^2 H_1^2 T_1 T_2)^{1/2}$ and ..."

49   Since the Kramers-Kronig theorem, Eq. (2.76), is only valid for linear systems, in which χ' and χ'' are independent of H_1, the remark at the top of this page is incorrect. Redfield [Phys. Rev., **98**, 1787 (1955)] has shown that in crystalline lattices χ' does not obey Eq. (2.65) although χ'' follows Eq. (2.66). Saturation of χ' sets in when $\gamma^2 H^2 T^2 \sim 1$, and not when $\gamma^2 H_1^2 T_1 T_2 \sim 1$. This also resolves the difficulty mentioned at the bottom of page 49.

50   Eq. (2.77): The lower limit of the integral should be $-\infty$.

53   Lines 23 to 25: The author's first experimental job in nuclear magnetic resonance was to poke a muddy mixture of oil and CaF_2 powder through a small hole in the cavity.

72 9th line from top: The shape of the resonance curve in an aqueous solution is Lorentzian.

4th line from bottom: Read "when" instead of "it."

75 The facts mentioned at the top of this page provided the foundation for high-resolution nuclear magnetic spectroscopy.

76-78 This discussion has only qualitative value. The saturation behavior in the presence of modulation and inhomogeneity of the magnetic field can be exceedingly complex. Numerous papers have been written on the subject [compare, e.g., Halbach, Helv. Phys. Acta, **27**, 259 (1954), or Hubbard and Rowland, J. Appl. Phys., **28**, 1275 (1957)]. Instead of attempting a complicated theoretical analysis of the saturation data, one should use the superior spin-echo techniques, which allow direct experimental observation of the true relaxation times T_1 and T_2. The author had a rather lucky, highly subjective approach of interpolating between the long times, reliably observed by direct decay and the very short times which are also rather reliable, because the Bloch steady-state solutions, Eqs. (2.65), (2.66), and (3.24), are valid for homogeneously broadened lines with $T_1 = T_2 \ll \omega_s^{-1}$.

83 Eq. (4.2): The statistical average of the left-hand term should have been indicated.

84 Eq. (4.5): The left-hand term should be the time average, which is assumed to be equal to the statistical average. Only ergodic, stationary Markoff processes are considered.

85ff. In the literature one often encounters statements that the BPP theory is not applicable in a certain fluid. The formulation of the relaxation mechanism in terms of the frequency spectrum of the local field density is, however, quite general. What is meant in such cases is that the Debye model does not describe the motion of the molecules in that fluid adequately.

87ff. According to the correction in Eq. (2.53), the numerator in the second term of Eqs. (4.15), (4.19), and (4.21) should be "$4\tau_c$" instead of "$2\tau_c$." Equation (4.25), derived from Eq. (4.21), needs modification of the numerical factors.

89 3rd line from top: Read "it is" instead of "is is."

91ff. Equation (4.22) does not give the correct behavior in the limit of small τ_c. Equation (4.27) is consequently incorrect. Equation (4.29) should read $T_2 = T_1$. See the comments on the theory of the line width on pages 42 to 44.

97　16th line from bottom: Read "concentrations" instead of "frequencies."

100　The line shape is Lorentzian. Later measurements have confirmed that T_2 and T_1 are approximately equal in Fe^{+++} solutions, but that $T_1 = 7T_2$ in Mn^{++} solutions. This has been explained by the consideration of a scalar spin coupling [see N. Bloembergen, J. Chem. Phys., **27**, 572, 595 (1957)]. The author was lucky that he picked Fe^{+++} rather than Mn^{++} solutions while working on his thesis.

105ff.　Spin-rotational interactions will also occur in liquids. Only recently has this topic received attention.

108　8th line from top: The value of γ for He^3 was assumed. The correct value may be found in reference A5.

7th line from bottom: Read "The probability per unit time for such a transition is given by (4.41)."

109　Between Eqs. (4.43) and (4.44): Read "$\cos \vartheta \approx 1 - H_1^2/2H_0^2$" instead of "$\cos \vartheta \approx 1 - H_1^2/H_0^2$."

116-118　The spatial averaging is inaccurate. If the acoustical wave does not propagate along the radius vector connecting the nuclear spins, the statement following Eq. (4.49) is incorrect. The proper method is, of course, to expand the dipole-dipole interaction into normal coordinates.

119　The note at the bottom of this page refers to the article in Physica which is also reprinted in this volume.

122　These data, taken in April 1947, represent the first evidence for nuclear quadrupole interactions in condensed matter.

The following comments apply to the paper "On the Interaction of Nuclear Spins in a Crystalline Lattice":

406　11th line from bottom: Read "I" instead of "S."

10th line from bottom: Read "S" instead of "ω."

Add a new line at the bottom: "$\mathcal{H}_{SI}$ represents the interaction between nuclear spins and impurities.

409　4th line from top: Add a dot to indicate scalar product of the vectors.

410　12th line from bottom ff.: Blumberg [Phys. Rev., **119**, 79 (1960)] has pointed out that the critical radius b should be determined by the condition that the local field is equal to $\gamma_{el}^2 \hbar^2 H_0 S(S + 1)(3kTb^3)^{-1}$, if the electron spin flips fast.

412   The borderline case of nearly identical spins with par-
      tially overlapping resonance lines has been discussed
      much later [Bloembergen, Pershan, Shapiro, and Art-
      man, Phys. Rev., 114, 445 (1959)]. The diagonal sum
      method of Van Vleck with appropriately truncated
      operators could also be applied to the case of spin
      diffusion. The factor λT_2 is essentially equal to $g_B(0)$,
      where $g_B(\nu)$ is the normalized shape function for a
      "flip-flop" process. The moments of $g_B(\nu)$ can be
      evaluated with the diagonal sum method by taking the
      commutator of the interaction term B in Eq. (7) with
      a Hamiltonian consisting of Eqs. (5) and (6), from
      which terms of the type C, D, E, and F have been
      truncated.

413   9th line from top: Read $W \approx (50T_2)^{-1}$.
      Eqs. (13) and (14): The left-hand terms should be pre-
      ceded by a plus sign.

414   Eq. (16): The term $D \Delta p$ should be preceded by a minus
      sign.

415   The solution of the spin diffusion equation has received
      further elegant analytical treatment from G. R.
      Khutsishvili [Publications of the Georgian Institute of
      Sciences, IV, 3 (1956)(in Russian)] and P. G. de Gennes
      [J. Chem. Phys. Solids, 3, 45 (1958)]. An approximate
      solution in closed form has been given:

$$T_1 = (8.5)^{-1} N^{-1} C^{-1/4} D^{-3/4}$$

      This analytical solution agrees well with the numeri-
      cal solution mentioned in the text. The conditions of
      validity of this solution have been discussed by Blum-
      berg [Phys. Rev., 119, 79 (1960)].

416   It was not appreciated that serious pursuit of the sugges-
      tion mentioned in the last paragraph would have led to
      the Overhauser effect and dynamic nuclear spin po-
      larization.

417   The qualitative ideas in Section 6 have been pursued more
      fully in a paper on cross relaxation between spin sys-
      tems already mentioned in the comment on page 412.

420ff. For further discussion and results, compare the refer-
      ence mentioned in the comment on page 410 and Chap-
      ter 9, Section II, of Abragam's book.

426   Reference 18, Physica, 19, 181 (1953).
      Reference 26, Physica, 10, 95 (1950).
      Reference 29, Physica, 15, 588 (1949).

Lecture Notes on
THE MANY-BODY PROBLEM
from the
1961 BERGEN INTERNATIONAL SCHOOL OF PHYSICS
Edited by Christian Fronsdal

THE N-BODY PROBLEM
by D. L. Falkoff, Brandeis University

THEORY OF SUPERCONDUCTIVITY
by L. N. Cooper, Brown University

ELECTROMAGNETIC PROPERTIES
OF SUPERCONDUCTORS
by Vinag Ambegaokar, Institute for
Theoretical Physics, Copenhagen

SCATTERING BY IMPURITIES IN
METALS
by G. Rickayzen, Chadwick Laboratory

DENSE ELECTRON GAS
by L. Mittag, University of Utrecht
and CERN

THE DIAMAGNETIC SUSCEPTI-
BILITY OF AN ELECTRON GAS
by M. J. Stephen, Oxford University

PROPERTIES OF THE NUCLEAR
SURFACE LAYER
by L. Rosenfeld, Nordita, Copenhagen

COLLECTIVE MOTION IN NUCLEI
by G. E. Brown, Nordita, Copenhagen

SUPERFLUIDITY IN NUCLEAR
MATTER
by J. S. Bell, CERN

ELIMINATION OF THE HARD
CORE
by J. S. Bell, CERN

THE ANALYTIC STRUCTURE OF
MANY-BODY PERTURBATION
THEORY
by Amnon Katz, Weizmann Institute

THE MOMENT OF INERTIA OF A
MANY-FERMION SYSTEM
by Amnon Katz, Weizmann Institute

THE LINEAR RESPONSE FUNC-
TION OF A MANY-BODY SYSTEM
by A. J. Glick, Weizmann Institute

THE T-MATRIX AND THE
CANONICAL TRANSFORMATION
by R. Balian, Centre d'Etudes
Nucléaires de Saclay

320 pp.   6 x 9   Paperbound $8.50

1961 BRANDEIS SUMMER INSTITUTE
LECTURES IN THEORETICAL PHYSICS

COMPLEX VARIABLES IN
ELEMENTARY PARTICLE THEORY
by R. J. Eden, Cambridge University

STATISTICAL PHYSICS
by R. Glauber, Harvard University

ELEMENTARY PARTICLE PHYSICS
by J. J. Sakurai, University of
Chicago

RELATIVISTIC QUANTUM ME-
CHANICS
by E. C. G. Sudarshan, University
of Rochester

RENORMALIZATION THEORY
by G. Källén, University of Lund

PLASMA PHYSICS
by M. Krook, Harvard University

ANALYTIC PROPERTIES OF
PERTURBATION THEORY
by J. C. Polkinghorne, Cambridge
University

THEORY OF POLARIZATION
PHENOMENA
by M. E. Rose, Oak Ridge National
Laboratory

RELATIVISTIC PARTICLE
INTERACTIONS
by E. C. G. Sudarshan, University
of Rochester

Volume I   About 350 pages   Approximately $3.50
Volume II   About 400 pages   Approximately $4.00
6 x 9
Paperbound

1960 BRANDEIS SUMMER INSTITUTE
LECTURES IN THEORETICAL PHYSICS

SELECTED PROBLEMS IN
GENERAL RELATIVITY
by C. Møller, University of Copenhagen

GROUP THEORETIC AND ANAL-
YTIC PROPERTIES OF SCATTER-
ING AMPLITUDES
by P. T. Matthews, Imperial College,
London

FIELD THEORY METHODS IN
NON-FIELD-THEORY CONTEXTS
by J. Schwinger, Harvard University

THE MANY-BODY PROBLEM
by N. Fukuda, Tokyo University
of Education

PROBLEMS IN STRONG INTER-
ACTIONS
by J. J. Sakurai, University of
Chicago

503 pp.   6 x 9 $3.50
Paperbound

THE THEORY OF FUNDAMENTAL PROCESSES
by R. P. Feynman
California Institute of Technology

A Lecture Note Volume. Covers the following topics: Superposition of Amplitudes, Spin and Statistics, Rotations and Angular Momentum, Spin 1/2, Relativity, Electromagnetic and Fermi Couplings, Gravitation, Nuclear Forces, Isotopic Spin, Pion-Nucleon Coupling, Strange Particles, Some Consequences of Strangeness, Strong Coupling Schemes, The Decay of Strange Particles, Universal Coupling Coefficient, Rules for Strangeness Changing Decays with Experiments, Scalar Particles and the Transition Probability, Density of Final State, The Propagator for Scalar Particles, Principle of Least Action, Particles of Spin 1, The Relation between Virtual and Real Photons, Scattering by Photon Exchange, Cospinors and Contraspinors, Extension of Finite Mass, Properties of the Four-Component Spinor, Compton Effect for Particles of Spin 1/2, Direct Pair Production by Muons, Higher-Order Processes, Self-Energy of the Electron, The Lamb Shift, Meson Theory, Decay of a Polarized Neutron, The Universal Fermi Interaction.

184 pp.   6 x 9   Paperbound $3.50

1959 BRANDEIS SUMMER INSTITUTE
LECTURES IN THEORETICAL PHYSICS

THE QUANTUM THEORY OF
SCATTERING
by F. E. Low, Massachusetts
Institute of Technology

FIELD THEORETIC METHODS
by J. Schwinger, Harvard University

WEAK INTERACTIONS
by E. C. G. Sudarshan, University of
Rochester

THEORY OF SUPERCONDUCTIV-
ITY
by L. N. Cooper, Brown University

HARD SPHERE BOSE GAS AND
LIQUID HELIUM
by K. Huang, Massachusetts Institute of Technology

COLLECTIVE MOTION IN MANY-
PARTICLE SYSTEMS
by H. J. Lipkin, Weizmann Institute

407 pp.   6 x 9 $3.00
                            Paperbound

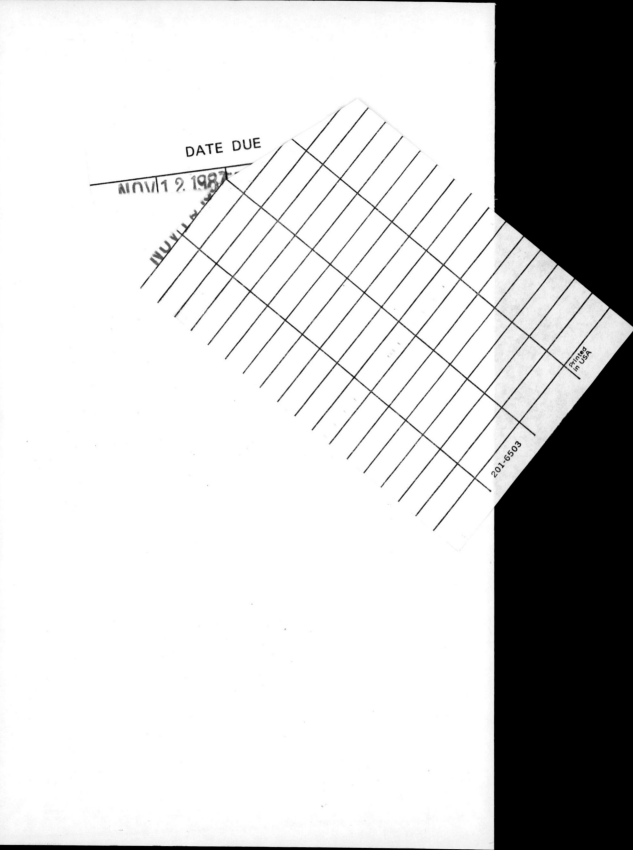

DATE DUE

NOV 1 2 1987

201-6503

Printed
in USA